Active Steps to Reducing Stress®

Published by:
Bracken Books
1, Crescent Bakery
St Georges Place
Cheltenham
Glos.
GL50 3PN
England

Email (for orders and Customer Service enquires): info@brackenbooks.co.uk
Visit our home page on: www.brackenbooks.co.uk

Copyright ©2008 Bracken Books, Cheltenham, Glos, England.
All rights reserved. No part of this publication may be reproduced, stored in a retrieval
system or transmitted in any form or log any means, electronic, mechanical, photocopying,
recording, scanning or otherwise, except under the terms of the Copyright, Design and
Patents Act 1958 or under the terms of the licence issued by the Copyright Licensing
Agency Ltd, 90 Tottenham Court Road, London, W1T 4LP, UK, without the permission in
writing of the publisher. Requests to the Publisher for permission should be addressed to
the publisher, Bracken Books, 1 Crescent Bakery, St Georges Place, Cheltenham, Glos, GL50
3PN, England or emailed to info@brackenbooks.co.uk

A copy of the British Library Cataloguing In Publication Data is available from the British
Library.

Trade mark: Active Steps is a registered trademark of Koch and Koch and may not be used
without permission.

ISBN 978-0-9559962-0-7
Designed by Studio Diva Ltd, Bristol.
Printed and bound in Great Britain by Stoate and Bishop Printers Ltd., Cheltenham,
Glos.

Important Note
Do not use this as a substitute for medical advice or treatment. Any person
with a condition needing medical attention should contact a qualified medical
practitioner or suitable therapist.

Active Steps to Reducing Stress

Life skills for feeling calmer

James Koch and Hugh Koch

Bracken Books

Author's acknowledgements

We would like to thank many friends and colleagues who have given us invaluable feedback, suggestions and support.

Francis Lillie	Sue Koch
Jeanette Koch	Emily Koch
George Walker	Simon Gourlay
Jacquie Hetherton	Alex Morton
Paul Elson	Ann Simmonds
Lyn Wright	Richard Mathers
Hazel Long	Steve Holder

In addition, many thanks to Julie, Sarah, Caroline and Andy.

This book is dedicated to Sue and Emily.

Contents

Introduction About this book

Welcome to Active Steps to reducing stress. In this book we look at practical ways to feel calmer on a regular basis whether at home or at work. If you approach the ideas we talk about with an open mind, and try out as many of them as you can, you will soon be feeling calmer and more in control of your day-to-day life.

To get the ball rolling we've answered some frequently asked questions we have encountered when talking to people about this book. We'll then discuss briefly our approach and how best to use this book – this will be helpful so please don't skip it!

You'll then be ready to get cracking on Section 1 and begin learning and practising lots of great stress-busting techniques.

There is an accompanying CD that has a 20-minute guided relaxation exercise inside the back cover. This will be discussed later in the book.

i) Frequently asked questions

Should we reduce our stress?

Stress and the feelings that go along with it occur everyday. This could be at home, at work and when we're out and about. If well managed, it is a part of getting things done, challenging yourself and coping with difficulties. For example, we all regularly need to cope with the stress of a busy day ahead. This can be well managed in a variety of ways: a good night's sleep, preparation for the day, good time management and positive thinking. This is a normal situation, which we all encounter from time to time.

However, poorly managing the above situation will only make the feelings of stress worse. Continued experience of stress is uncomfortable and unhealthy. It is important, therefore, to learn how to control stress whenever possible. Developing an alternative to continued stress and anxiety results in many benefits including improved physical health, energy and motivation plus enhanced relationships, feelings of well-being and control.

Throughout life, we are likely to experience significant overload (when we feel we have too much to do), intimidating new situations (such as an interview or a difficult new project), worrying everyday events (an argument), and very occasional crises (such as bereavement or redundancy).

Many of these cannot be prevented, but our ways of coping with them can be improved, giving us greater self-confidence for dealing with future events.

Can a self-help programme work?

All self-help books set out with the same aim – to help the reader improve a particular health or life issue. If, as is often the case, the reader experiences positive change through self-help, they will not only feel the benefit of the improvements they have made, but also have gained the extra confidence of knowing that they did it for themselves. For a self-help book to work we not only need the initial motivation to pick it up, but also to read it, practise the new ideas and persist with them when we find they work. These new skills will stay with us if we keep using them.

We are not saying that by using this or any other book we can gain complete control of our life or our stress. Life *is* difficult, and will continue to be so. But it is not helpful to get stuck in a rut – thinking and doing the same things, the same way, day after day, and feeling the same way too. We need to be open-minded to new ideas that can help, and then give them a go.

What is the 'Active Steps....' series?

This is a collection of books covering common health and lifestyle topics. We hope that each one will inspire you to improve actively and positively four crucial areas of living – your thinking, lifestyle, communication and behavioural skills, to help you fulfil your health and life goals. The series emphasises your own ability to manage your health and uses non-medical language. The ideas are simple, practical, yet effective – for fast and long-lasting results. This is the first of the series.

Who are the authors?

We are psychologists who have an interest and experience in helping people improve their health and healthy behaviour using practical ideas which work.

James Koch

I'm a psychologist living in Bristol. I developed a keen interest in health and fitness from an early age. I represented England at rugby and Wales at hockey at junior level. Having gained a degree in psychology I spent the next few years setting up and running my own businesses in the leisure industry, spending much of my time in pubs and clubs in line with my work. This was great fun but I developed some habits along the way, which contributed to my own feelings of stress and anxiety.

Researching, writing and testing out the Active Steps approach has helped me identify what works for me. I try to stay focussed on the things that help me feel calm and I spend much of my free time keeping fit and pursuing my creative passions: music and photography.

I hope some of the ideas in this book can help you too.

Hugh Koch

I am a clinical psychologist in Cheltenham. Over many years I have developed a positive, solution-oriented approach to helping people with mental health problems. I had previously worked as a hospital manager and am currently a director of a medico-legal firm. I have spent time with people in a variety of settings finding practical steps they can take to solve their personal problems and feel less stressed.

Looking back on my early family life, it was happy but stressful and I had an underlying level of anxiety, which I learnt to manage using techniques, which we are now writing about. I have been married for 32 years. I like playing guitar and keeping fit by running, cycling and the occasional triathlon.

We are both keen to make 'psychology' ideas more available and understandable – we believe there are many straightforward techniques that we can all use to feel better in our everyday lives. Throughout the book we will explain how we reduce our own stress when we think this will help illustrate a point.

How does it work?

This book uses ideas taken from 25 years of research in the UK and USA into cognitive-behavioural therapy (C.B.T.) and other solution-based approaches. C.B.T. is widely acknowledged as crucial to understanding how psychological difficulties are caused, maintained and treated both within the public health (N.H.S.) and private health sectors. Although other approaches are practised, C.B.T. is the main psychological therapy endorsed by the N.H.S. National Institute of Clinical Excellence (N.I.C.E.).

What is an Active Step?

Reading this book will not in itself make you calmer. You will need to actually put the good ideas in this book into *action* in order to experience and maintain the benefits. An Active Step (or *AS* for short) is a technique to help you develop a more proactive ability to manage your stress and feel more confident about doing so. The aim, with each Active Step, is to make it clear what you can *do now* to make a start on each topic in this book. This means, literally, today and tomorrow. We hope that this will help you get started on making the changes you want to. After all, it's often getting started that's the most difficult part of any task.

You may feel that we are stating the obvious with some of the Active Steps. But that is the point – they are straightforward. Getting started and completing any task can be easier if you break it down into small chunks that you complete one at a time, starting at the beginning (today) and progressing bit-by-bit. This approach - identifying the first Active Step to complete a task - can be applied to stress and most other areas of our lives. We can start to think in this way in order to get us started and 'on the road' to our desired destination – wherever, whatever that may be. Don't worry too much now about what an Active Step is – it will become quite clear as you read on. We will explain how to use them throughout the book.

ii) The 'Active Steps' approach

Although you, the reader, will need to do most of the work, we have tried to write the book in a way that will help you to succeed. Here's what we think works best:

A *positive* approach

We will help you focus on your goals, your strengths and what you can do in the present and future rather than dwelling on the past. How we want to feel and what we want to do is more achievable if we think positively and expect success. Being positive is a great talent we all have in different amounts - we will try to help you feel more positive, energetic and inspired about aspects of your everyday life. Positivity is infectious – see how it spreads.

A *practical* approach

We describe the information clearly and concisely using everyday language. To get you started, we suggest a series of tasks in the form of Active Steps.

An *active* approach

To start experiencing benefits, you will need to put the ideas in this book into action. And the sooner you do, the sooner you will start to feel the benefits. To help with this, the Active Steps throughout the book show you what you can *do now* to get started on each important topic. More and more we want you to adopt an active approach both in what you are doing (the action) and when you do it (now).

As you are reading the book, experiment with as many Active Steps as you can. Even if you just try out one or two, this will lead to some immediate benefits today and tomorrow. At the end we will discuss ways to bring the Active Steps together into coherent plans.

A step-by-step approach

Usually, we can only achieve lasting change by making small steps, one at a time. Completing one step and feeling the benefit helps make us more motivated and encouraged to try the next one. This will build up your momentum gradually. It will require patience, determination and lots of practice - but it will be worth it.

A TLCB enhancing approach

TLCB stands for thinking (T), lifestyle (L), communication (C) and behaviour (B) - these are four key components of healthy living and working. In different ways, we do these things all day, everyday, and they strongly affect how we feel. They can make us feel bad (stressed) or feel good (calm). Soon you will be an expert in each of these areas. You may be wondering why we've shortened it to the TLCB acronym. Well, we will regularly refer to these four areas as a combined unit throughout the book. For successful stress control they *all* need to be addressed. We hope using the TLCB acronym will help you to remember these four areas, and the importance of them being used *together*.

An action planning approach

Remember: the *action* is what will actually make the difference – taking the ideas in this book off the page and bringing them to life. A clear *plan* will help you remember when, where and how to do this so that you don't forget, and so that you keep making progress in the short and longer term. Don't worry about this too much now, we will help you design your own action plans later in the book.

iii) How to use this book

After you have finished reading the introduction, there are six main sections to the book. Section 1, *Motivation to reduce stress*, will prepare you for getting started with the core information. This comes in sections two to five, covering the key areas of everyday living which help stress-control – your thinking, lifestyle, communication and behaviour (your TLCB).

Thinking to reduce stress

Different techniques to make you mentally calmer are discussed in this section, in the context of increasing your positive, logical and mindful thinking.

Lifestyle to reduce stress

Everyday areas of nutrition, health, exercise and managing home/work balance and environments are outlined.

Communication to reduce stress

It feels good to talk to people and to give and receive positivity and warmth. This section will show you how to help others help you.

Behaviour to reduce stress

Many practical strategies are outlined to help you get better organised and to relax more often and more deeply.

Because we are going to ask you to try out a few small tasks (Active Steps) as you go, we recommend that you allow yourself one week to experiment with each of these four sections. We don't want you to feel overloaded. We do want you to try out as many Active Steps as possible. Allowing yourself one week per TLCB section will help you achieve this.

Finally, in Section 6, we help to organise your new skills into workable plans for continued benefit.

The four TLCB sections – thinking, lifestyle, communication and behaviour, contain a total of 16 steps, which cover the main components of stress management. Each particular step is made up of a number of specific topics and culminates in a practical Active Step per topic, for you to try straight away. If you give the Active Step a go, we suggest how you can continue to make progress on the topic, *this week* .

Remember – we advise you to take one week between reading each of the TLCB sections to allow yourself the chance to have a good go at each section.

We will explain this further throughout the book.

iv) Tips for success

Soon it will be time to get started on Section 1. Before you do, though, here are a few pointers to help you get the most out of the book:

Think what works, and when
We all have problems with managing stress. What do you *do* when you feel a bit stressed? It's natural that you will *do something,* but does what you do actually help, or is it unhelpful - only serving to fuel your stress in the long-term?

There are ideas in this book that we can use if we start to feel a bit stressed, in order to help us feel calmer again (reactive). There are also ideas that we can use on an everyday basis - to help reduce our stress in the longer-term (proactive). Most of us use these ideas to some extent, but quite often we are not aware we use them, or of their benefit, and so don't use them consistently. We may also tend to mix them up with unhelpful TLCB (thinking, lifestyle, communication and behavioural) styles, which reduce their benefit.

As you read this book, start thinking what your own TLCB approaches have been in the past. Have any of your own TLCB approaches been helpful? Plan to use them more often. Have any of them been unhelpful? Consider working on reducing these. Throughout the book we will help you identify what these helpful and unhelpful approaches are and how to persist with or change them.

Experiment with changes
You may already have tried some stress management techniques included in this book, and can use this book to further reinforce your determination, confidence and ability to be calmer wherever you are. If you discover some new ideas, you can experiment with the Active Steps provided to see how they work for you. So, as you read on, try identifying some topics you already use, and some you can immediately try out through their Active Steps. Look out for the *AS* sign throughout and give them a go. By persisting with the familiar ones and experimenting

with some new ones, you will immediately feel a bit calmer and more confident. Allow yourself one week to read and experiment with each of the TLCB sections.

Be positive: visualise success

Train yourself to see the positive side of things more and more. Once you start on Section 1, get into the habit of seeing what is good about the different ideas we talk about.

Throughout the book we will ask you to visualise yourself in certain situations. When we talk about visualisation we mean imagining what it would be like to do something. For example, if you wanted to get a bit fitter – can you imagine what that might be like? How might that feel? Well, for a start you would feel healthier. You would probably sleep better and feel more positive and confident in your own abilities. You are likely to feel more alert, energetic and motivated at home and at work. With this in mind, can you picture what this might feel like for you? Feels good, doesn't it?

Visualising success, whether in how you feel or what you do, can help make it happen, as it increases a feeling of positivity, self-belief and desire to make it so. Use this technique more and more from now on to picture yourself achieving *your* goals.

Be patient, not perfect

Experimenting with some of the Active Steps in this book will help you feel calmer and more in control of your day-to-day life. In fact, the more Active Steps you manage to have a go at the better. We will be discussing ways to enhance your TLCB (thinking, lifestyle, communication and behaviour) in order to feel calmer, healthier and happier.

But, be patient! Don't put pressure on yourself to achieve amazing results immediately. Don't expect yourself to become the Dalai Lama, a finely-toned athlete, the world's best communicator AND a multi-millionaire *overnight*. In fact, it's unlikely that any of these (let alone *all)* will end up happening to you or us. These examples aside, no-one is perfect or should expect to be perfect.

Becoming calmer and feeling more in control of your everyday life *is* achievable for all of us, however. So, have this as a realistic goal over the next few days, months and years. Find the balance between challenging yourself enough that you push yourself to progress, but stop short of expecting too much, too soon. Focus on enjoying the process of each AS you try out. Set yourself lots of realistic mini-goals. Soon you *can* be *more mindful, more active, a more positive communicator and more in control of your finances.* All of these are achievable, don't you think? Be patient, recognise every small improvement you make and don't worry about making mistakes. If one of the steps isn't going 100% to plan, don't worry or give up – take a breather, reassure yourself that you can do it, take the positives out of what you have managed to do so far and give it another go. Success can be just the other side of frustration.

Talk about it

Don't forget to talk to your family, friends and colleagues about what you are doing. Talking through ideas with others helps. They will be interested to hear about your stress-reducing techniques and may be able to share with you their own experience, both good and bad. Is there someone you know who you think manages stress particularly well? If you talk to them about how they think they do this, you'll probably find that they already use some of the techniques talked about in this book. Is there someone you know who you think struggles to manage stress? Discuss one or two of the ideas in this book with them – they will find this helpful. It feels good sharing ideas with others. After all, soon you will be an expert in stress control.

Feel more in control

Make feeling more in control of your everyday life your first target, with this in time leading to a feeling of increased calmness. We can all feel that our work and home lives are a bit out of control sometimes, in a mess – and that's what contributes to the feelings of stress. By following the instructions in this book, we will help you take 'control of the reins' and feel more confident managing all of the different demands that are placed on you. This is achievable – you can do the things you need to do, and more of the things you want to do, and feel more positive, relaxed and healthier in the process.

So! It's time to get started on this journey of yours

1) Read through the book, thinking positively about the ideas we talk about – they will work for you if you give them a go.

2) Experiment with as many of the Active Steps as possible. Try things out straight away as you are reading the book or once you put it down. How do the Active Steps make you feel?

3) If you're not so sure – be patient and give them another try.

4) If they make you feel good, keep using them.

5) Feeling calmer and more in control is just a few Active Steps away.

Section 1 Motivation to reduce stress

We know that you are already motivated to learn about managing your stress control.

> *In this section we will help you increase your motivation further by encouraging you to:*
> ✓ *Understand when you get stressed and what this feels like.*
> ✓ *Recognise the benefits of stress control.*
> ✓ *Set yourself some helpful goals.*

Even though you are probably keen to make a start on Step 1, please read this section before you begin. It will help give you a stronger foundation to build upon.

At the end of each topic there is an Active Step (**AS**). Take a few minutes to complete each **AS** before moving onto the next topic. They are typically multiple choice questions and do not take long. There are no right or wrong answers – it is not a test. This is to help further increase your understanding of your relationship with stress, and increase your motivation to enhance this relationship, for good.

As you go through the **AS** in this section, keep your conclusions firmly in your mind, especially the goals that you set for yourself.

In this and the four TLCB sections, we will introduce you to someone different who has been experiencing feelings of stress on a regular basis and is now reading Active Steps to Reducing Stress to help them.

Jean

Hi, my name is Jean and I am 45 and married, with two teenage children. I often used to feel stressed out and didn't understand why this was. It caused me a lot of worry. I ended up worrying about the worry – which really tired me out. I also felt quite confused. Was I suffering from stress? I didn't know much about stress at the time, and didn't know why I might be feeling it so much and what I could do about it if I was.

When I got stressed out, I'd get different physical feelings in my body like my muscles tensing up, sweating and even my heart racing. Sometimes I was aware it was because of stress, but often I would worry there might be something wrong with me that I wouldn't be able to change. These experiences made it difficult for me to be with other people, as I felt better off being on my own. My mind went round and round and I felt awful.

I used to wish I could manage stress better, like my husband – he has always seemed to thrive on pressure and used it to get things done and to achieve more. When I was going through a bad patch, I couldn't see the wood for the trees – I felt physically and mentally drained, lacking in energy and got very little done. I would rarely feel calm or motivated.

The worst thing about the way I felt was that I didn't know what to do about it. My life had been drifting for a while at this point and I wanted to get back on top of things and feel calmer and more in control. I remembered that I used to be like this when I was younger.

One day, a friend of mine recommended I read Active Steps to Reducing Stress. I read Section 1 – Motivation to reduce stress – hoping to learn a bit more about stress, and about my stress in particular.

We'll hear how Jean gets on later in this section.

i) Understand more about stress

Do you know why you get stressed, what this feels like and even when this stress can be helpful to you?

Why?

Stress occurs when we think the pressure we are under is more than we can cope with.

This may occur when we are facing:
- ✓ General overload – too many things to do or think about.
- ✓ A new or challenging situation – such as an interview, unfamiliar task, new experience or specific fear.
- ✓ An unhappy event – such as a big bill, argument with a partner or friend or poor exam result.
- ✓ A crisis – like a relationship break up, divorce, death of a loved one or redundancy.

The single most intense form of stress may be a crisis. For most people, however, it is the constant build up of everyday pressure, which at times feels overwhelming, that leads to the experience of stress.

Recognising and knowing why you typically feel stressed can help you work out more effective ways of feeling calmer.

For example, if you are overloaded, time management, logical thinking and relaxation techniques might be useful. If you have a difficult interview, good preparation and positive thinking techniques will come in handy. If you are having difficulty paying your bills, better financial planning skills may be of use. If you are faced with a crisis such as a relationship break up, social support will be vital to you.

Whilst this is over-simplifying solutions to each of these situations, you can see how each different situation will require a slightly different response so it's good to understand your own stress triggers and responses as best you can. We will look at example action plans for de-stressing each of the above situations later in the book (see Appendix, page 291).

While you are reading this book, think why you get stressed and also think which steps, topics and *AS* might help you feel calmer.

Think of a time in the last week you felt particularly stressed. Why was this? Please circle below or write alternative answers underneath:

Too much to do at home	Overloaded at work
Feeling criticised	An interview
Financial problems	Disorganisation
A difficult journey	An argument
Relationship problems	Feeling you've done something badly
Untidy home	Poor health
Redundancy	Death of a loved one
Fear of the future	Fear of not being able to cope
Fear of letting other people down	Feeling lonely

What?

We experience stress on at least three different levels:
Physical – such as muscular tension, sweating and increased adrenalin.
Thinking – when you are nervous, worried, negative, pessimistic
or have difficulty thinking straight.
Social – wanting to be alone or approaching others for support.

It will usually be a combination of all three, which can become a *vicious cycle of stress* that is difficult to break.

For example, if you think in a worried way, this makes you feel physically anxious and then this affects the way you deal with people around you.

Up until now, you may not have been very aware of what stress actually feels like. Once again, it can be helpful to recognise this.

We will look at ways to deal with all three aspects throughout the book.

Circle below on what levels you mostly experience stress:

Physically

Thinking

Socially

Helpful stress

Stress or pressure is useful if it is managed carefully.

For example, anxiety felt *before* an interview, exam or unfamiliar journey, if managed well, can result in more planning which helps to deal with the event and get better results.

Alternatively, if not managed, it could lead to continued worrying, inaction and increased discomfort, resulting in poor performance or mistakes.

With stress, the key is to try and stay 'in control' as much as possible and not let it get on top of you.

Visualise being able to helpfully manage stress in the future to complete an up-and-coming task. Making this a reality will not only mean you feel calmer and less stressed, but will also help you get things done more efficiently.

This is achievable – we will show you how you can do it.

AS

In which of the situations below could you use your stress constructively?

Planning a journey

Monitoring your finances

Preparing for a difficult day at work

Tidying up

Revising for an exam

Maintaining happy relationships

Keeping up a healthy lifestyle

Resolving a difficult issue

Looking after your family

Jean

I used to find it difficult to understand what was causing me to be stressed or to link my unpleasant experiences to stress. This made me feel that my life was out of control – I felt helpless and vulnerable.

I now understand more about how stress affects me mentally, physically and in my relationships. Although I am surprised by how much I am affected by stress, I am relieved that at least I know that it is stress that is causing it.

Knowing more about what stress actually is makes me think about what I could do to reduce my stress levels.

I'm hopeful that I can soon turn a corner and feel more in control of my life.

ii) Appreciate the benefits of stress control

It helps to know about the benefits of controlling stress, but also to be aware of the risks and disadvantages of continuing to feel tense or stressed.

Risks of stress

There are a number of unpleasant consequences of continued stress:
- Depression.
- Low self-confidence.
- Lack of social interaction.
- Loss of sexual energy and interest.
- Lack of sleep.
- Poor performance at work.
- Susceptibility to colds and flu.
- Psychosomatic disorders (e.g. stomach ulcers, skin complaints, raised blood pressure).
- Tension headaches.
- Fatigue, lethargy and low energy.
- Susceptibility to physical illness.

To help motivate yourself to put the Active Steps in this book into practice, read this list again now and recognise the ones you have experienced in the past 3 months. Remember why you are reading this book – to keep these risks at bay.

Benefits of stress control

Developing an alternative to sustained anxiety and tension can deliver a number of benefits:
- ✓ Regular calmness and well-being.
- ✓ Improved physical health.
- ✓ Extra energy and motivation.
- ✓ Resistance to infection.
- ✓ Increased concentration and attention.
- ✓ Better communication and relationships.
- ✓ Success with work and life goals.

Visualisation is a powerful tool to help you feel confident about your goal. The more you can picture yourself enjoying each of the above benefits of stress control, the more you will feel motivated to practise the *AS* in this book day-by-day.

The more you practise the *AS*, the more you will start to experience the benefits of stress control.

Circle and imagine enjoying the specific benefits of stress control. Increased and improved:

Calmness	Energy	Motivation	Confidence
Happiness	Concentration	Attention	Sleep
Sexual appetite	Relationships	Communication	Physical health
Success at work	Fulfilment of life goals		

Jean

Until now I didn't know how stress was affecting me. I thought the headaches and my poor sleep were just something that I'd have to get used to – down to me and for me to deal with. I didn't think that they could be due to something else – something to do with stress. To know that by reducing my stress I can reduce these symptoms, and also increase my confidence, motivation to get things done and general calmness is great. I'm excited because this will make a big difference to me in all sorts of different ways – my home life, my work, my social life and how happy I am generally.

I don't normally go for 'self-help' because I've never felt the need or seen the point. If putting the ideas in this book into practice means that I can start to enjoy some real benefits, however, I'm willing to give them a go.

iii) Set your goals

Having a clear idea of where you would like to get to *emotionally* (how you would like to feel) and *vocationally* (what you would like to do with your life) is crucial for a positive outlook, and increases the chance of you actually making it happen.

How do you feel when you are stressed?

Understanding how you have been feeling will give you more insight into what you need to do to feel calmer. It will also allow you to be more aware of when you are feeling better, and how this has been achieved. This in turn will reinforce the positive changes you are making and make it more likely you stick to them and remain more in control of your stress. This does work.

In Table 1 (opposite), put a cross next to any of the negative effects you feel stress has on you. Do you recognise any of them? The 'X' means you intend to get rid of these effects.

Fill in the first column of Table 1 on the opposite side of the page now. Put a cross next to the effects of stress that *you* feel.

How would you like to feel?

You can and will change your feelings of stress into calmer, more positive ones with the help of this book. Imagine that you no longer feel the pressure of sustained stress and its consequences on your day-to-day life. How would that feel?

In Table 1 below, tick in the second column how you would like to feel. Be positive and visualise what each of these changes would be like. There is room underneath to add any other ideas.

Table 1

Effects of stress I feel		How I would like to feel	
Tense and not in control.	☐	*I am calm and in control.*	☐
Generally pessimistic.	☐	*Optimistic about my own abilities and future.*	☐
Negative thinking.	☐	*I think positively.*	☐
Illogical thoughts and language.	☐	*I use logical and constructive thoughts and language.*	☐
Anxious visualisation.	☐	*Calm and positive visualisation.*	☐
Nervous and constantly on edge.	☐	*I am relaxed and 'laid back'.*	☐
Inability to sit calmly and appreciate my environment.	☐	*Ability to be mindful and appreciate all my senses calmly.*	☐
Difficult to relax fully.	☐	*Feel confident in my own ability to relax whenever and wherever I am.*	☐
Muscular tension.	☐	*I feel relaxed and at ease.*	☐
I shut myself off from family and friends.	☐	*I have regular supportive communication with family and friends.*	☐
I've let myself go a bit.	☐	*I feel fit, healthy and good about my appearance.*	☐
Don't have enough time to do what I want to do.	☐	*I have enough time for work and family tasks as well as to exercise, maintain a calm home, eat well and relax.*	☐

What would you like to do?

Once you feel more in control of your everyday stress, you may become more focussed on your own life goals. These may be personal or family based, ambitious and risky or basic and secure, financial or vocational, short-term or long-term, or a combination of the above. We do not want you to worry about achieving these goals and put extra pressure on yourself to get there, as that could make you *more* stressed and defeat the object of this book.

It is, however, useful to be focussed in a positive way on what you are setting out to achieve when you get out of bed in the morning. This will also give you extra incentive to put into practice the stress-busting *AS* in this book.

In Table 2 (overleaf), tick some shorter-term and longer-term life goals that you would like to set yourself. Many of these may have previously been only sub-conscious. It will be a good exercise for you to see them on paper and make you think about what first steps you can take to make them happen.

You don't need to pick out too many. But don't worry if you end up ticking most of them – this book will help with each of them.

Fill in Table 2 with your life goals now. Tick a mixture of things you can do today as well as longer-term objectives. Visualise living each of your goals and be optimistic about achieving them.

Table 2

Things I would like to achieve:

Make more time for myself.	☐	Feel more relaxed and positive.	☐
Build and maintain better relationships.	☐	Get fitter.	☐
Become more focussed at work.	☐	Drink less alcohol.	☐
Feel more socially confident.	☐	Afford a nice holiday.	☐
Take up a new hobby.	☐	Reduce the amount of junk food I eat.	☐
Get off benefits.	☐	Make my home a tidier, more organised and calmer place.	☐
Find a partner.	☐	Stop smoking.	☐
Feel healthier.	☐	Become more successful at work.	☐
Have more disposable income to spend.	☐	Spend more time being creative.	☐
Pay off debts.	☐	Learn to play a musical instrument.	☐
Move house.	☐	Spend more time with friends.	☐
Raise children to the best of my capabilities.	☐	Save money for a rainy day.	☐

Time to get started

The greatest motivation of all for you to reduce your stress levels will be for you to get started and begin to feel some benefits.

We want you to learn and practise the *calmness response* instead of *the stress response*. Regular practise will reduce many of the negative effects of stress, open you up to the benefits of feeling calm and allow you to focus more on your life goals.

The most important thing is that:
- ✓ You try something (e.g., an ***AS***).
- ✓ You try it today, tomorrow and the next day.
- ✓ You find it makes you feel good (a bit or a lot).
- ✓ You want to try this again.
- ✓ This makes you then want to try another ***AS***.
- ✓ And so on...

This sets up a 'positive cycle' of increased calmness and breaks the 'vicious cycle' of stress.

Refer back to the motivational Active Steps in Section 1 if you feel you need to remind yourself of the benefits and goals you are striving for. We hope that you are now really motivated to fulfil these. We will help you get started.

Take a minute now to read again all the Active Steps in this section, and how you have answered them. This will give you extra impetus to get started on Section 2 – *Thinking to reduce stress.*

Get used to using a small amount of time (like a minute) to do something constructive, like the Active Step above. It will make you feel energetic and 'achieving' and doesn't take long.

Jean

I now understand a lot more about stress and how this has affected me recently. Now I know how I would like to feel. For instance I would like to feel more at ease with myself - more 'laid back'. I'd also like to feel good about my appearance and be generally more confident, positive and relaxed. I can picture what this might be like, which gives me a warm feeling inside.

For the first time in a while, I have also made some short-term and long-term goals for myself. I plan to make more time for myself and also take up a new hobby — learning to play the guitar. I am more determined than ever to learn the calmness response and start achieving the goals I have set myself. I know that, with help, I can do it and that when I do, there will be no stopping me!

I'm open-minded to try out some new ideas. I'm going to break this cycle of stress and start feeling better. Life's too short!

Summary Motivation to reduce stress

Well done on finishing the first section in this book.

Having read Section 1, you should now feel that you have a better understanding of *your stress*. We hope you are now also clearer about how you would like to change this, for the better, always.

We hope that you have completed all the *AS* and are now feeling even more motivated to feel calmer. If you are unsure about this, perhaps you might want to read this section again, retry the *AS* or discuss them with a friend.

Use this summary to remind yourself of your motivation to become calmer, and to encourage you to persist with the positive changes you are about to make.

Understand stress
Understand why you become stressed.
Understand what stress makes you feel like.
Understand when stress can be helpful.

Appreciate the benefits of stress control
Appreciate the risks of stress.
Appreciate the benefits of stress control.

Set your goals
How would you like to feel?
What are your short-term and long-term life goals?

Great stuff! It's now time to get started on the first of the TLCB* sections -*Thinking to reduce stress*.

*Thinking (T), Lifestyle (L), Communication (C) and Behaviour (B).

Section 2 Thinking to reduce stress

We spend approximately 16 hours a day thinking.

Whatever we are *thinking* about has a huge effect on how relaxed or stressed we *feel*.

Quite often we can create a feeling of pressure and stress through thinking in an anxious, negative, pessimistic, illogical and generally unproductive manner.

We all do each of these to some extent, but by reducing them we can become calmer.

This is a powerful tool – simple and incredibly effective.

In this section we will look into how:
- ✓ You can feel calmer and more confident by thinking more positively.
- ✓ Thinking logically makes sense.
- ✓ Using calm imagery relaxes the mind.
- ✓ Mindfulness can help you feel contented.

To help get you started, we give you an Active Step(*AS*) at the end of each topic. These are meant for you to do straight away as you are reading the book. What we suggest you can do next, to continue making progress on each topic, is marked this week. Try and put this into practice, over the next week, before you start reading the next section.

If you find that the ideas in this section work – keep using them!

There are four steps in this section. As we mentioned in the introduction, allow yourself a week from when you *finish* reading this section to when you *start* reading Section 3. This will give you the opportunity to persist with the ideas we talk about, before we give you more to try.

In the first two steps, we will occasionally ask you to write something down on your *affirmation card.* This can be found near the back of the book on page 307. Write on this page to start with. You can cut this out. If you want, you could copy this on to a thicker card which would be more robust. Affirmation cards are a great way to remind you to think positive thoughts about yourself and your day. This card can be kept on you during the day.

Please write down what we suggest, or something similar, on your card as you go along. It won't take much time at all to do and it will make a big difference if you do it. We will discuss how you can make best use of your affirmation card throughout the book.

Positive *thinking* skills will help you *feel* a lot better.

They will also have a knock-on effect on your *motivation* and ability to improve your *lifestyle, communication* and *behavioural* skills.

Improving each of these will in turn reinforce your positive *thinking* skills.

This positive cycle of increased calmness and control can soon be yours.

Omar

My name is Omar. I'm 35, and live in a rented house with my wife. I have been an estate agent for five years now. I have several friends but my relationship with them is often difficult. I have come to realise that my stress tends to be caused by the way I think negatively about myself, other people and my life in general.

I often feel helpless, especially when things around me don't go well. For example, when I wake up I will think nervously about the day ahead and predict that if something goes wrong, I will not be able to do anything about it. I usually don't feel particularly positive, optimistic or in control and don't know what to do about it.

When I'm at work, I presume that the viewers will probably dislike me and the property I'm showing them around. Sometimes it just feels like I don't get anything right – all I do is mess things up. I know that this isn't actually true, though. If I am expected to do extra hours at work, I will never say anything to my manager, even when I've got something planned that evening. I think that if I do, my manager will dislike and criticise me.

All my negative ways of thinking have gone unchallenged for some time now. I realise that, up until recently, I wasn't even aware of them. Even now – I'm not sure I can change them. Friends tell me that I tend to predict 'gloom and doom' and exaggerate how bad things are. I ignore difficult situations. For instance, instead of preparing for a recent meeting, I left it until the last minute and panicked. Instead of setting about solving a problem with one of the properties, I took a day off, hoping someone else would sort it out.

My relationships at work can be variable. If I think someone at work doesn't like me, or I fall out with someone – to me, this is a disaster. On the one hand, I blame others and am highly critical of them and, on the other, I am hard on myself too.

When I get stressed, my mind either races or goes blank – the thoughts and images in my head are anxious ones, telling me, 'It's gone wrong, is going wrong and will go wrong'. Quite often I find I'm beating myself up about past events or stressing myself out about my future. I have great difficulty digging myself out of this rut and focussing on 'now'. Sometimes I just can't motivate myself to keep going.

At least I recognise that I am a negative thinker and that I have things to work on. I am keen to find out what thinking techniques I can try out to feel better. I'm willing to give them a go, as I'm tired of feeling like this.

We will be following Omar and his progress as he uses the 'thinking' steps to try and reduce his stress.

Step 1 Think positively

Much of the time, we feel calm, relaxed and in control. However, sometimes it can feel that life, either at home or at work, or both, is just a series of stressful or negative events waiting for us around each corner that we have no ability to avoid or alter.

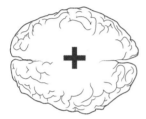

This feeling of helplessness and negativity can lead to an ongoing stream of stressful feelings. To help change this, we want to help you develop your positive and assertive thinking. Remember you are more in control of how you think, feel and what you do than you are aware of.

Whether you think about your 'whole self' or think about doing one specific task, it is always helpful to have positive thoughts about your capability. These *thinking* techniques are incredibly effective and will help you start to *feel* more in control of your life and calmer as you go along.

Throughout this step we ask you to write positive affirmations down on your affirmation card (p307). Once you have finished reading this first step, and written on the first side of your affirmation card, read the card regularly. You can keep it on your bedside table and say the affirmations first thing in the morning and last thing before you go to bed. Or you could keep it on your person, on your desk or clipboard. We will discuss practical ways to use this card throughout the book.

Even if you're not sure about doing it, please give it a go because it will help. The more you read the card, the more you will start to believe and feel the things you have written.

In this step we will help you to:
- ✓ Be more confident.
- ✓ Be more optimistic.
- ✓ Focus on the positives.
- ✓ Be assertive: express yourself.
- ✓ Recognise your everyday successes.
- ✓ Reassure yourself.

Be more confident

Inner belief makes it easier to get things done.

This is either with the small things, or with the bigger things in life. **Lack of inner belief makes us continually question and stop ourselves from committing and moving forwards.**

When we believe in ourselves, many things are possible.
If you tell yourself often, and believe that you will become a calmer and happier person, it is more likely to happen. Think and talk positively about your own ability to get things done on an everyday basis.

Tell yourself: 'I can do this' in a clear, calm and positive inner voice. You will come to accept this, which will help to make it so.

You have the ability to increase your feelings of calmness and control. Be confident that you can start, and then continue, to achieve the goals you have set yourself whether they are daily, weekly or longer-term.

You can do many things well already. You can also challenge yourself and successfully try and learn to do new things.

Be confident in your own ability to get things done today and tomorrow.

James says:
I recently went on an evening class. On the day I started I found myself getting really nervous about attending and I almost talked myself out of going. What I found helped was to write out a list of some of my positive attributes and all the reasons I should go to the class. Reading this out several times made me feel more confident about myself and attending the class, which I did and it was great.

Be more confident about your own ability to get things done. Write down I can do it now on side 1 of your affirmation card (p307).

Write down below 3 things which you have done well today or yesterday, no matter how small they may seem:

1. ....

2. ....

3. ....

This week

Confidently approach each task you tackle, no matter how small or large. Read your affirmation card twice through, first thing after you have woken up in the morning. Read it in a clear and confident inner voice, or if you are on your own, out loud. Carry it on your person for use during the day – you can keep it in your wallet, purse, handbag or diary.

Be more optimistic

A self-fulfilling prophecy.

What is optimism? Having positive expectations about a task, our day or our future.

How can being more optimistic help me to feel calmer? More optimistic people are usually less anxious and less prone to stress.

Can optimism actually make a real difference to my day? Yes – being more optimistic will help you feel more positive, energised and motivated to get things done. Being more optimistic can change the way you feel about your day *and* how your day actually turns out.

How can I become more optimistic? You can practise with your own thinking and also how you talk to other people.

Ever heard of a self-fulfilling prophecy? Things will go wrong from time to time for everyone but *even more so* if you *expect* things to go wrong! Be more optimistic, more of the time, and you will find that things turn out well, more of the time.

Start to practise being optimistic with the little things in the present. This could be a phone call or a job you need to do. If you expect it to go well and think optimistic thoughts, your positive approach means that it is more likely to go well. You can then move on to bigger things such as future events or long-term goals.

Experiment with being more optimistic every day. **At this point, you may think, 'Oh, that's obvious'. It is – the difficult thing is to remember to tell yourself minute-by-minute to be more optimistic.**

So, approach your next job at home believing it will be OK. **Think of your next job at work and be optimistic that it will turn out well too. Doesn't this feel good?**

Try it and see.

> James says:
> For me, optimism is a good example of how all the ideas in this book combine to positive effect. I often go through patches where I don't feel particularly optimistic. When I try and work out why, I often find that I have been drinking too much alcohol, not sleeping well, not exercising and not keeping in touch with friends and family. All these things combine to de-energise and de-motivate me which results in me thinking negative and pessimistic thoughts. Staying balanced and motivated helps me feel optimistic about my day and my future.

Be more optimistic about your next task, your day and your week. Write down Today is going to be a good day now on your affirmation card (p307).

Which 3 tasks have you got to do today or tomorrow, however small?

1. My next task is:

2. Today I need to:

....

3. Tomorrow I need to:

....

Think optimistic thoughts about how these will turn out now.

This week

Approach each day, each task and each different situation you tackle with optimism. Read your affirmation card twice through after you have your breakfast each morning. Talk optimistically!

Focus on the positives

If you look for the positive things in life, you will find them.

Why be critical? It's easy to be critical of yourself, and it's also easy to be critical of other people. This could be towards family, friends, colleagues or people we don't actually know too well at all. When you think about it, this doesn't help us to feel calmer and it often probably isn't fair.

We ALL have faults, and for all *their* faults, we still love our family and friends, respect our colleagues and want to help and support them. We also want them to *help and support us too*. Being critical of them isn't the best way to achieve either of these goals.

It's easy to criticise or judge people we don't know, but because we don't really know them, it is often even more unfair and inaccurate!

Criticising is probably something we all do. Perhaps we feel that by identifying apparent 'faults' in other people it makes us appear better people to others and to ourselves?

What's the bigger picture? Try and remind yourself to *keep things in perspective* and to look at *the bigger picture.* If you are feeling critical about a friend, this might mean remembering the length of time you have known them and all the *good things* they have done in that time. They may have done something to annoy you *today,* but have been consistently good friends beforehand. Of course, this can be applied to other relationships. It can also be applied to your view of yourself and your own life.

Focussing on the positives takes this approach a step further. Doing this doesn't mean pretending that problems don't exist or that everything is perfect. But you will feel calmer and more able to cope with issues that crop up if you keep in mind all the good things about you, other people and the situation, especially the small things.

It feels good to be positive about ourselves and others. Practise focussing more on the positives today.

Hugh says:
I worked with a colleague in Colchester who would usually find the positive in most situations. He inspired me to try this out more and more. Even when things seem bleak, there is always something that's good and can make you smile and keep going. Even if the glass is empty, you've still got a glass!

Focus on the positives. Do this for a moment now – think of some of the good things about you and what you have done today. Make these small things. Write down two of these below. Also write down Focus on the positives on your affirmation card (p307).

One thing I like about myself

....

One thing I like about my day so far

....

Remember to focus on the positives each day, even (and especially) when you are feeling a little down or stressed. Read your affirmation card twice through each day when you stop for lunch.

Be assertive: express yourself

"I want to become a calmer person!"

It's important that we feel able to express our own opinions and personality freely, whilst still allowing others to express their own opinions and personality freely too.

This means thinking for ourselves and acting in a way that is true to us, not automatically agreeing with somebody else's viewpoint or automatically doing what other people might do or expect us to do.

So, how can you be more assertive today?
- ✓ Try and practise making clear '*I* statements' about what you think, what you feel and what you want.
- ✓ If you are unhappy with something someone has done or said – tell them how you feel... carefully (about what they have *specifically* done or said).
- ✓ Remember – friends and colleagues appreciate straight talking. You don't need to be pushy or aggressive.
- ✓ If you are feeling under pressure at work – talk to your manager about it and see what he or she can do to help. (If you feel it would help, ask for more training, less workload or additional assistance).
- ✓ If you haven't got time to stop and speak to someone on the phone or in the street – politely tell them so, calmly and with a smile.

What makes you *you*? We are all individuals after all. We all have slightly different backgrounds, interests, passions, beliefs and styles.

What's your 'style'? Whilst a certain level of social conformity is appropriate - such as being polite and considering each other's feelings - we should also feel free and able to be uniquely 'us'.

Being assertive and expressing yourself will help prevent the build-up of frustration, resentment and unhappiness by not being able to express who you really are and how you really feel.

This will make you feel good, **and can also help you get the things you want and need.**

It's fine to be different. It's good to be an individual.
It's great to find out, and be, who we really are, and express how we really feel.

'I want to teach'   'I need a holiday'   'I want to be a footballer'   'I want to do an Open University course'   'I love the Spice Girls'

James says:
Finding out who we really are can be a long process. Don't swim against the flow. Spend time finding out more about the things and people that interest you and pursue your passions. Just because you don't make a living out of them now, doesn't mean that you won't be able to one day....

AS

Be assertive: *express yourself.* Write down Be assertive and express yourself now on side 1 of your affirmation card (p307). Write down below 5 things that you feel make you *you.* What are your interests, beliefs, origins?

1.

....

2.

....

3.

....

4.

....

5.

....

This week

Make clear '*I* statements' about what you think, feel and want. Read your affirmation card twice through when you stop for a mid-afternoon break each day.

Recognise your everyday successes

Do you realise that each day you achieve many different things?

Whether we are at home or work, we can often feel under too much pressure to have time to stop and acknowledge the fact that we have finished something before moving on to what's next.

Get into the habit of recognising all your everyday achievements. Do this on completing a task, before you move on to the next one.

This is satisfying and will help you feel more positive about yourself and your day.

Don't forget what you have done for yourself and for others. Every now and then take a little time to remind yourself of all the good things you have done in the past (this morning, yesterday, last week...). Whilst you don't want to dwell there too much, these things are all successes, no matter how small:

- ✓ Completing the washing up.
- ✓ Doing a food shop.
- ✓ Sending an email.
- ✓ Phoning a friend.
- ✓ Going for a walk or jog.
- ✓ Smiling at someone in the street.
- ✓ Making a start on a big job.
- ✓ Posting a letter.
- ✓ Taking an interesting photo.
- ✓ Texting a friend to see if they are OK.
- ✓ Preparing a meal.

It's important to take time to recognise some of the things that you have done well each day. If you do this, it will feel good.

Hugh says:
When I've got a lot on, I find that it helps me a great deal if I acknowledge what I finish, even if it's just a small job. This gives me energy to keep going. It could be in the garden, at work or sorting out the house paperwork. No one sees me patting myself on the back except me, but it helps.

Recognise your success: **Make a list of some of the things you have completed and done well today and yesterday. Write these down below:**

1. ....

2. ....

3. ....

4.
....

5.
....

If you are finding this difficult, it may be because you are looking for the BIG things. Go for the small things: they are always there.

This week

Throughout each day, take some time to recognise your successes. Feel good about what you have achieved, especially the small things.

Reassure yourself

Be your own best friend.

Be as supportive to yourself as you are to others. Most people are caring and supportive to the people they are closest to – friends, partner and relatives. Don't forget the person you are closest to – YOU!

Don't give yourself a hard time for difficulties you face or mistakes you may have made. If you talk negatively to yourself, you will start to feel worse.

Everyone has difficulties and makes mistakes – learn from them and programme yourself to think positively about yourself even when you feel things haven't gone well.

Practise talking reassuringly to yourself on a day-to-day basis from now on and see how that makes you feel – whether you're at home or at work.

It helps you to feel more confident and able to carry on with your day.

Talk positively to yourself: start to think and act like you are your own best friend.

James says:
If I find I am doubting or criticising myself, I try to stop and think one or two positive thoughts about myself. I then try and distract myself with something else to do or think about.

Reassure yourself today in everything you do. If something goes wrong, be positive and supportive to yourself. 'Watch' your actions but give yourself positive feedback about what you do. Write down Be my own best friend now on side 1 of your affirmation card (p307).

This week

Be your own best friend, reassuring yourself positively if something goes wrong or you feel a bit low. Read your affirmation card twice through each evening when you get in. How does this make you feel?

Identify, challenge and change negative thoughts

You will only be able to increase positive, calming thoughts and reduce negative, stressful thoughts if you are aware of them.

Do you think and talk down to yourself? Have you noticed that, on occasions, you are negative or pessimistic and don't believe in yourself or express yourself freely?

It can quickly become a habit leading to regular feelings of helplessness and stress.

It is possible to put a stop to this anxiety and negativity by listening out and *identifying* these negative thoughts, *challenging* them and getting into the habit of immediately *changing* them to positive, calming thoughts and comments.

Here's an example: You wake up one morning and are nervous about your day ahead at work. As you make your breakfast you start to think about your day ahead and say to yourself:

'I *can't* go to work today - it will be awful, what's the point?'
This in turn makes you *feel* more stressed and unhappy.

So, what can you do?

1) Identify.
This is clearly a negative and pessimistic statement.

2) Challenge.
Is what I said really true? No
Am I being negative and pessimistic? Yes
Can I go to work? Yes
Will it be so awful? No
Will work be better if I approach it in a positive and optimistic way? Yes
Will I *feel* better if I approach work in a positive and optimistic way? Yes
Will I feel better in the long run if I go to work? Yes

3) Change.
'I *can* go to work today – I will feel better once I'm there and once I have finished for the day. It will be worth it - I can do it!'

Imagine thinking positively like this more and more – would that make you feel good?

Watch your negative thoughts today. Identify and challenge negative or pessimistic thoughts. Practise this now – what negative thought or comment have you had or made today? What could you change this to? Write down Identify, challenge and change negative thoughts on side 1 of your affirmation card now (p307).

This week

Monitor your thinking for any negative thoughts you may be having. Challenge any you identify and change them to more positive, productive ones. Read your affirmation card twice through before you go to sleep each night.

Getting started on Step 1....

...Today, tomorrow and this week: read your affirmation card first thing in the morning after you wake up, and at regular intervals throughout the day. You can do this if you keep it on your person in a pocket, wallet, diary or handbag. Watch your thoughts throughout the day and ensure that, more and more, they are positive, optimistic and productive. Be assertive when you are at home, at work, out and about and when you are on the phone. Reassure yourself if something goes wrong and recognise all of the little successes you have each and every day.

Omar

I've been trying to adopt a more positive attitude to my life since starting the 'Active Steps' programme. I have begun to practise 'thinking about thinking'. When I wake up, I think about my day ahead and make a positive prediction – 'today is going to be a good day'. I am also experimenting with saying to myself 'I can do this' regularly. Sometimes I'm not sure if I believe it, but nevertheless I say 'I can do this' about whatever it may be, over and over again in a clear and confident inner voice. I have found that it makes me feel a bit more confident and optimistic, which is good.

I recently had to present some sales figures to my manager and, instead of worrying excessively about it, I told myself it would be OK... and, with some preparation, it was. I have begun to express my opinions and views more and not be too scared what others might think or say. The more I do it, the more confident I feel.

One thing that's been really useful is to practise remembering what has gone well each day and telling myself I'm doing a good job. Sometimes I write a list at the end of the day. Even with small things, I have found that this makes me feel good. I am beginning to see how some of my old negative, pessimistic thinking has made me seem a gloomy person – I now look for chances to think and talk positively about things.

Even my friends have noticed the change. I realise now that I can do those everyday things that I was concerned I couldn't. In fact, with my new positive thinking style I am starting to approach each day more with hope and expectation than fear.

I still have good days and bad days, but more good than bad now.

Step 2 Think logically

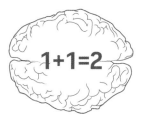

Everyday events are not always easy to explain rationally, but if we think logically more of the time, this helps a great deal to reduce unnecessary stress. What we *think* and what we *say* has a big effect on how we *feel*. Logical thoughts make us feel relaxed and more in control. Illogical and worrying thoughts have the opposite effect.

When we are logical, things usually work. When we are not, they usually don't. We can control this a lot of the time by asking ourselves on an everyday basis if our thoughts are as logical or rational as they might be. How logical do you think *you* are?

Write down affirmations from this step on side 2 of your affirmation card (p308).

These are the topics in this step:
- ✓ Be specific, don't exaggerate.
- ✓ Make positive predictions, don't catastrophise.
- ✓ Face facts.
- ✓ I am what I am and that's OK.
- ✓ Solve problems.
- ✓ Understand others' actions.
- ✓ Don't overreact emotionally.
- ✓ Distract yourself.
- ✓ Keep an open mind.
- ✓ Identify, challenge and change illogical thoughts.

Be specific, don't exaggerate

Question: If you tell a friend about having had an argument with someone, how do you describe the other person?

*Answer 1: She is so stupid - she's **always** arguing with me; I don't like her **at all**!*

*Answer 2: She's a good friend to me. I disagreed with **something** she said but these things happen. We all say silly things **sometimes.***

Everyone exaggerates a little. But try not to use excessively negative or extreme language. The problem is if we believe our illogical words, it can make us feel more stressed, especially if we exaggerate, generalise or think that things are too black or white.

Practise being more specific. When being critical of someone else try not to talk or think about the problem being them as a person who *always* does or says something you dislike. Instead describe what they did – *their actions* - which were difficult in one particular circumstance.

Don't exaggerate the frequency in which problems occur. The word 'always' is usually inaccurate and makes the problem seem much worse and more difficult to sort out.

James says:
I try and listen out for when I might be exaggerating and stop and correct myself where I can. I do this even if it's just in my thoughts.

Be specific, don't exaggerate: **Write down** Be specific: don't exaggerate on side 2 of your affirmation card now. Can you remember a recent difficult situation where you have either exaggerated a problem (did this help?) or were actually quite specific (this helped, didn't it?).

This week

Read your affirmation card twice through first thing in the morning after you wake up. Use it to remind yourself to talk about specific actions that friends and colleagues do, and aspects of situations rather than whole people and whole situations. Remember to carry the card on you each day.

Make positive predictions, don't catastrophise

Question: How would you describe your feelings about an upcoming event, which you are nervous about?

*Thought 1: It's **bound** to be an **utter disaster**!*

*Thought 2: As long as I **prepare** properly **it will be fine**.*

Think logically. If possible, think, "this will be OK – I've handled something similar before"; or, "what can I do to make it OK?"

Preparation will help. In the above example, the logical thinker in Thought 2 identifies what needs to happen in order for the upcoming event to go well.

Don't resign yourself to failure. By thinking or saying, "yes it might be OK, but....", you are expecting things to go wrong. This can result in anticipating it in a negative way and getting yourself unnecessarily worked up.

Practise making positive and logical predictions.

Being positive not only means you will be feeling calmer but also makes this positive outcome more likely.

Being logical will stop you from panicking and help you decide how best to proceed.

> Hugh says:
> Going into court on a particular case can be nerve-wracking. I prepare properly beforehand. I tell myself that I know what I'm doing, I will be able to answer most of the questions fired at me and, with any difficult questions, I should be able to come up with a sensible answer, as I have done in the past.

AS

Make positive predictions, don't catastrophise in your thoughts and when speaking to people. Call somebody now to catch up and talk about your and their day in a logical and positive way. Write My day will go well if I think logically on side 2 of your affirmation card now.

This week

Make positive predictions throughout each day about any work, journeys, meetings or activities you have coming up. When you talk positively about something, how does it make you feel? Read you affirmation card twice through after you have had your breakfast.

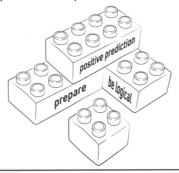

Face facts

Question: How do you approach a bad debt or money problems you are not sure how to sort out?

*Answer 1: I'll **leave** it until next week to sort out **and pretend** nothing's wrong.*

*Answer 2: **The sooner** I face up to it the quicker I will get it sorted and **the better** things will be.*

Health, wealth or happiness issues can be applied to this example.

For example: if you think you may be ill - but are too scared to see a doctor – you could be wasting valuable time and only get more ill in the long run. Alternatively, if there is nothing wrong, you could be worrying for no good reason. Either way, talk to a doctor and find out!

You may be worried about your finances, as in the example at the start of this topic. Face facts and look for help and advice, either through your bank, free financial advice (The Consumer Credit Counselling Service – freephone 08001381111; The National Debtline – freephone 08088084000) or even friends and family. Step 12 looks at financial matters in more detail.

If you think you have a drink or drugs problem, but are not sure, there are lots of helplines that you can call which are free and anonymous (Drinkline – 08009178282; The UK National Drugs Helpline – 08007766000). Call one of them for a chat, they are friendly and helpful. Step 6 looks at managing alcohol intake in more detail.

Try not to bury your head in the sand and expect that your problems will just disappear overnight.

Putting things off usually only makes matters worse. In the meantime you are left with nagging worry and fear.

Hugh says:
Sometimes when I'm going through my finances, either at work or at home, I come across a 'gremlin' - some large bill I didn't know existed. I've learnt now not to ignore or hide it away. I tell myself that there will be a way to sort it out if I think carefully without getting upset. Holding my nerve helps!

Face facts: Write down below any *health, wealth or happiness* issue you want to work on to help you feel calmer. One health, wealth or happiness issue I would like to sort out is:

....

This week

Take the first Active Step in dealing with the issue you have written down above by describing it to yourself and by talking it through with a friend.

I am what I am and that's OK

Question: It is your 60th birthday – what do you think? (NB for 60 substitute your age!)

*Answer 1: Oh **misery**, 60 years old! I hate being this old!*

*Answer 2: Let's **celebrate**! I've had lots of **good times** and I will have lots more, including **today**!*

It is healthy to feel good about yourself as a person and to accept who you are. This inner self-belief helps us to accept and express our thoughts and feelings openly and with confidence.

It's also healthy to want to change certain aspects of yourself. We all want to learn and grow.

Work on developing your own habit of contentment, at the same time as you are developing new positive and stress reducing skills.

Practise accepting who you are. The more you do so, the easier this contentment becomes. From this acceptance of who and where you are *now*, you can continue to make the positive TLCB* changes you want to make to improve yourself for *tomorrow*.

Use walking through a doorway to spark this off. Sometimes you can use an everyday action to help begin a new way of seeing things. For example, every time you walk through a doorway, whether it be at home, work or out-and-about, practise having positive 'accepting yourself' thoughts. Breathe in, keep your head up and feel good about yourself.

Although you can become more positive, skilled and knowledgeable, you will never be perfect, so don't put too much pressure on yourself to be perfect. Remember, nobody is perfect.

Thinking logically, some things simply can't be changed, such as our past or growing old.

James says:
I sometimes find myself getting caught up in things that are not my fault or that I cannot change. To help me stop thinking about these things I try and think of some of my good points from someone else's point of view. I try and remind myself that I'm alright really, despite all my imperfections.

* TLCB: Thinking (T), Lifestyle (L)... do you remember what C and B stand for?

Feel good about yourself now. Get up and walk through the nearest doorway. As you do – keep your head up, breathe in and think to yourself, I am a good person. Write this down on the back of your affirmation card too.

This week

Use walking into a room, building, office or shop as a trigger for feeling good about yourself. Get into the habit of remembering to say positive things to yourself regularly. Read your affirmation card twice through each day before you have lunch.

Solve problems

Question: How do you approach a problem or difficult decision that needs to be made between several choices?

*Thought 1: This is **too much** – I **can't cope**. I **don't know** which way to turn!*

*Thought 2: Maybe **my** own problem-solving **skills** can **work**?*

Next time you have a problem that needs solving, stay calm and take a few minutes to apply these six steps:

1) Describe the problem – thinking to yourself, talking to someone or writing it down

2) Brainstorm possible solutions – have you been in this situation before – if so, what worked or didn't work? Get ideas by asking yourself how you would advise a friend or colleague coming to you with the same problem.

3) Think about what's positive or negative about each solution.

4) Choose the best option.

5) Do it.

6) Review how it went and, if necessary, revise your strategy.

You will make some headway, but if you are still undecided you could talk to someone about it to gauge his or her opinion.

Problem-solving helps you to organise your thoughts in a systematic and focussed way.

Thinking logically, this helps you to come up with positive workable solutions whatever the situation and wherever you are.

Hugh says:

Nearly every problem has a solution of some sort. I do a lot of my problem-solving for work on the 'back of an envelope', often on a train. I use exactly the words and stages above. I do it on the way to and on the way back from somewhere so I've had a chance to re-think what ideas might/might not work. I get through lots of envelopes!

Use problem-solving techniques: Take a couple of minutes now to apply the 6-step problem-solving plan to your health, wealth or happiness issue from the earlier 'Face facts' *AS* .

1 Describe

2 Brainstorm

3 Think

4 Choose

5 Do it

6 Review

This week

When you are faced with a problem, apply the 6-step problem solving plan.

Understand others' actions

Question: If a friend of yours walks past you in the street without saying hello or is snappy on the telephone, do you think:

*1: How rude, **I** haven't done anything to deserve that. **I'm** not speaking to him again!*

*2: That's not like **him** – I hope **he's** OK. I'll **call him** later to check.*

Don't jump to your own conclusions why people behave in a certain way.

Consider *they* may be feeling stressed, unhappy or they may have a negative type of thinking or talking style themselves which affects how they behave towards people, including you.

Approach them to see how they are feeling – they will probably tell you about what's on their mind. They will also appreciate your concern.

You will feel good about the way you handled the situation and see yourself as a more sensitive and understanding person.

Try not to take other people's actions too personally or presume why someone says or does something.

Thinking logically, you can't know until you ask. And there's no point stressing yourself out unnecessarily.

James says:
More often than not, I find that when I jump to conclusions – I'm usually setting myself up for a fall!

Understand others' actions: Take a second now to consider the actions of someone close to you, which frustrated you. Consider how *they* were feeling. Could you have been more understanding?

This week

Try and understand and be considerate to how the people around you are feeling. If you sense that they may be worried, upset or stressed about something, offer your support.

Don't overreact emotionally

Question: You are having a bad day and feeling a bit low. You are asked your opinion on a girl you have just met for the first time:

*Thought 1: **That girl** really annoyed me.*

*Thought 2: **If I** wasn't in such a bad mood then **I'm sure we** would **get on fine**.*

Sometimes emotions can cloud thinking and lead to false judgements, so try not to judge situations based only on how you feel.

Try and remain calm and positive. Even if you are having a bad day, feeling angry or fed up, watch out for the way you think, speak and behave towards yourself and others.

You will start to feel better in time. In the meantime, others will respond better to you.

Don't give yourself or others a hard time because you are upset or down. Thinking logically, this may be undeserved and more due to how you are feeling than to something in particular you or they have done.

Hugh says:
A bit of logic, a bit of feeling. It's like pepper and salt – they are both useful but shouldn't overpower each other. I sometimes lose my rag and it doesn't help. Equally, just being sensible doesn't always make people warm to you either. You need both logic and feeling.

AS

Don't overreact emotionally: Recognise your feelings and don't let your emotions affect the way you treat people today. Write Don't overreact emotionally down on the back of your affirmation card.

This week

Be aware of how you feel, emotionally. If you are about to have an argument, ask yourself whether this is really necessary, or whether it's mainly because you are feeling down or upset. Take a deep breath and pause before saying something big or definite. This gives your brain more time to think. Also remember to read your affirmation card twice through at the start of each day.

Distract yourself

Question: If you find yourself thinking about something 'bad' in your past, or a problem today which you just can't solve, what can you do?

*Answer 1: I'm going to **keep thinking** about this problem and **sort it out**, even though it **doesn't seem to help**.*

*Answer 2: This **doesn't work** – I'm going to think about, or do, **something else** to take my **mind off it** and help me **feel better**.*

We can find that our thoughts go round and round **when we think about difficult things.** Once in this *maze,* sometimes there is no obvious solution to the problem, or exit, and we get more and more stressed as a result.

Take time out by distracting yourself **with other** *thoughts* or *actions.* This is very effective; it can involve thinking about something that makes you happy, or ordinary tasks you need to do next at home or at work.

You could do something like:
- ✓ Phone a friend.
- ✓ Some housework.
- ✓ Send an email.
- ✓ Go for a walk.
- ✓ A creative hobby.

You can then return to the difficult issue later with renewed energy and, often, a different perspective.

Don't give yourself a hard time, going over things again and again which are worrying you.

If it isn't getting you anywhere – have a break – and think or do something else.

Hugh says:
I'm not very good at practical DIY at home. If I am having difficulty sorting out how to assemble something (usually from a well-known Swedish store), I take a break, do something else which is easier and then return to the DIY task with new energy. If that fails, I shout!

Distract yourself from anxious or negative thoughts. Write down below one positive thought and one positive action you can use to distract yourself from such thoughts.

One positive *thought* I can use to distract myself with is:

....

One positive *action* I can use to distract myself with is:

....

This week

Use the positive thought and action you have written above (and any other ones you have) to distract yourself from anxious or negative thoughts.

Keep an open mind

Question: If you have an argument with your friend do you think:

*Thought 1: Friends **shouldn't** argue with each other, this **proves** we are not well suited.*

*Thought 2: It's natural to fall out **from time to time**, but I will make more of an effort not to in the future.*

Question any absolute beliefs you are having. In this situation, think about what happened and what was said, with flexible thinking.

Be careful using the terms *should*, *must* and *got to* as this all-or-nothing thinking can lead to unrealistic expectations, disappointment and stress.

Practise being open minded and logical about expectations you place on yourself and on others.

Cultures, religions and lifestyles may differ from one another in certain ways, but they also share much in common. Be open-minded about people and places that you may know little about.

Being more open-minded allows you to identify similarities you share with others and learn from different approaches or viewpoints. This can make the world seem a smaller, friendlier and less anxious place to be.

James says:
I try and stay open-minded about the music I listen to. I find that listening to a wide range of music and being interested in the musicians, their background and their inspiration keeps me open-minded to cultural diversity. It also shows how, despite geographical, cultural or linguistic differences, we are all very much alike.

Have an open mind. Think of someone who makes you feel judgemental or makes you think "he/she should....". What would be a more open-minded response? Write down Keep an open mind now on side 2 of your affirmation card.

This week

Question any preconceptions you have about other people and their different thoughts, beliefs and culture. Allow yourself to accept and be interested in the differences, not disregard or be afraid of them.

Identify, challenge and change illogical thoughts

You can begin to change how you feel by changing how you think - but first you need to know what illogical and unproductive thinking styles you use.

Watch or listen to your thoughts and your language when you speak. When you have *identified* illogical thinking, *challenge* it and *change* it to more logical and positive thinking.

Practise being as logical as you can. As a result you should feel calmer. If you believe this logical approach helps, then it's just a matter of practice. If you are not sure about this, try an experiment by being more positive and logical with yourself and others today and see what happens.

Does it work? It should help you feel calmer and more in control. You should get a good response from others.

Being logical helps you feel calmer.

Identify, challenge and change illogical thoughts.

Hugh says:
This is an interesting one for me. I usually feel I am reasonably logical, but the way I check this out is to ask other people around me what they might do in a particular situation, and this usually shows up how they may be more logical than me.

Watch your illogical thoughts today. Identify and challenge any illogical thoughts you have at home or at work or when out and about. Write down Identify, challenge and change illogical thoughts on side 2 of your affirmation card now.

This week

Monitor your thinking for any illogical thoughts. Challenge any you identify and change them to more logical, productive ones. Read your affirmation card twice through before you go to sleep each night.

Getting started on Step 2....

...Today, tomorrow and this week: Practise thinking in a more logical, productive way. Accept the things you may not like about yourself and spend that energy on facing up to the things you can change, using your problem-solving skills to make a start. Whether you are thinking about yourself, a situation or others, be specific, open-minded and understanding. Do this when talking to others too. Practise making positive predictions – no 'buts'! Ask yourself – "am I thinking logically?" and feel good when you do. Read your affirmation card clearly and confidently at regular intervals throughout the day – if you believe what you are saying it will help to make it so.

Omar

Looking back, I can see how my anxiety used to lead me to think in a negative and illogical way. But it was also my negative and illogical thinking that caused my anxiety. I guess they used to feed each other.

I now feel I am breaking that cycle. I have begun questioning whether the negative and anxious thoughts I have about myself or others really make sense or not. If not, why think them and get wound up? I find that the more logically I can think, the fewer anxious thoughts I have and the calmer I feel. I also find that the more positively I think and approach things, the more positive the outcome.

For example, I now wake up expecting the day to go well, rather than predicting that things will go horribly wrong. On the Tube I try to remind myself of the good things I have done recently and why I am a good person, rather than any mistakes I have made – what's the point in that? This increases my self-belief and sets me up for a good day at work. When I get to work, if I have any problems, I face up to them. I now use the 6-step problem-solving plan regularly – it works and it has made me realise that I am capable of coping as long as I try to stay positive, think straight and deal with 'problems' as they arise.

I have found that I am more open-minded when I talk to others and that I rarely overreact if something gets under my skin. I have been getting on better with my work colleagues as a result. I am trying to be more understanding of how other people may be different to me in certain ways and also to look at what I like and respect in them. I realise that my friends and colleagues are actually good people and am beginning to value them more.

I know that the more logically I think, the more positive and productive my thoughts are, and the calmer and happier I feel. This has really improved my situation at work and my social and home life too. I am beginning to feel more confident – I am determined to keep going with my new skills. I am also excited about trying out some more.

Step 3 Imagine calmness

In much the same way as our thoughts can have an effect on how we feel, so too can images we visualise alter our feelings as well.

You can use imagery to distract you from stressful situations, to reinforce positive thoughts and encourage more general calmness – they are very powerful.

In this step we will explain the different imagery-related topics through examples.

Each will contain 'when' to use each form of imagery and 'what' imagery you can use, including a specific 'example'.

We will then discuss 'how' you could visualise this image.

In this step we will look at how you can:
- ✓ Use calm imagery.
- ✓ Use coping imagery.
- ✓ Use motivation imagery.

Use calm imagery

- *When* – Caught up in a traffic jam, faced with a desk piled high with jobs or finding it difficult to get to sleep.
- *What* – Picture yourself in an easy place to relax.
- *Example* – Picture that you are in a garden on a summer's day.
- *How* – You visualise that the sun is shining and you can feel the heat on your face. The sky is blue and the grass green beneath your feet. You can smell the flowery scents of summer and hear the breeze rustling gently through the trees.

Do you ever wake up in bed, in the middle of a dream?
Sometimes you might be having a pleasant dream – in which case you wake up all relaxed, and feel like going back to sleep to continue the dream. Other times you may have a stranger, more worrying dream – from which you can wake up feeling anxious and tense.

This shows how the images in our heads can affect how we *feel*, even though this may be our sub-conscious and outside our control.

When we are not asleep we can control these images better.
So replace anxious, stressful images with calm, relaxed images wherever and whenever you can.

Calm imagery can help = a calm mind.

Hugh says:
Driving down the M5 in busy holiday traffic is not my favourite sport. If I get stuck in tailbacks, I will often use the surrounding countryside to occupy my thoughts (even though I'm concentrating on the caravan in front). It's funny how often these green images come into my head when I'm feeling stressed elsewhere.

AS

Use calm imagery: Try this out now - take a couple of deep breaths, let them out slowly.... and use your favourite calm imagery to relax you. What is that image?

Some calm imagery I can use to relax me is:

....

....

....

This week

Use calm imagery when you are in a stressful situation to help relax you. It takes less than a second to bring up an image in your mind and let this calm you.

Use coping imagery

- *When* – You have a speech to give, an exam to take or a difficult journey to make.
- *What* - Picture being able to deal with the situation.
- *Example* – Visualise giving a well-received speech.
- *How* – You visualise yourself 'in the room' and look around you at all the people there; you have prepared well and know what you are going to say; you speak clearly and confidently; when you finish people congratulate you on a good speech.

Do you find that sometimes you picture in your head things going wrong? For example, if you have an important call to make, do you ever visualise forgetting what you want to say, stuttering or saying something silly that you didn't mean?

It's normal to do this sometimes **when we are nervous, but this sort of negative imagery will only make us more nervous.**

Visualise yourself carrying out tasks successfully **if you have something to do that you are worried about.** Go through the different stages from start to finish; visualise yourself coping well with each stage.

Using coping imagery will help relax you and give you confidence that you can deal with the task at hand.

James says:
I try to picture things going well, people smiling, positive conversations and happy outcomes. I find it helps me feel good and makes positive outcomes more likely.

Visualise success: Take a moment now to visualise yourself successfully completing one task that lies ahead of you today. How does this feel?

This week

At the start of each day, and throughout the day, visualise yourself successfully completing each task you have to do before you have to do it.

Use motivation imagery

- *When* – You find that, on one particular day, you're losing interest and motivation at your workplace.
- *What* – Picture yourself doing what you would like to be doing in the future.
- *Example* – Visualise where and how you would like to be living in five year's time.
- *How* – Picture yourself in your preferred job or profession and living your ideal lifestyle. How does it feel? Won't it be worth all the hard work in getting there?

Do you ever feel like you are running out of steam? This could be at work, home or with whatever task you are attempting. Sometimes it can feel like we are not really 'getting anywhere'. Other times we can lose sight of why we are doing things, what we are aiming for.

We usually do things for a reason; you can keep this reason in your mind to help motivate you to keep going and get through your day.

You may be working to save up money for a holiday....
.... Visualise yourself on a beach lying in the sun....

You may be going for a run to get into better shape....
.... Visualise yourself feeling more comfortable in your clothing...

You may be giving your home its weekly clean....
.... Visualise sitting down when you have finished and relaxing....

Visualising positive outcomes can be a strong
motivational force.

It's good to know that we are doing things
for a reason, and to remember what these reasons are!

Hugh says:
I vividly remember when I was 28 and just getting bogged down in
my research project for my PhD in Leicester. I would often just make
my mind think about why I wanted to do this and how it would feel
when I got the final degree. This really kept me going in the early
hours of many a cold morning.

Use motivation imagery: **Visualise now what it would feel like to be calmer and more in control on a day-to-day basis.**

This week

Regularly visualise being calmer and more in control. How would this affect how you felt, your relationships and your lifestyle?

Getting started on Step 3...

...Today, tomorrow and this week: Focus on using positive images in your mind to make you feel calmer throughout the day. When you find yourself faced with either a) stress, b) a difficult job or c) de-motivation, use these feelings as a trigger for using helpful images or thoughts which bring on feelings of calmness, success and motivation. You can also try 'bringing on' these feelings at regular intervals throughout the day.

Omar

I used to find it very difficult to keep calm mentally, my mind raced and my thoughts and images were anxious and pessimistic – I felt I couldn't change this. I realise now that I made things worse by visualising stressful images and picturing in my mind negative outcomes to situations.

Having given the **AS** in this step a go, I now regularly use positive imagery to reduce my stress. On the way to work, I imagine what jobs might be waiting for me and visualise sorting them out. I also have my eye on a promotion and an increase in my basic wage. I think about what this would mean to me – maybe we'd be able to move out of rented accommodation and get a place of our own? I find this motivates me to keep working hard.

Whenever I'm feeling a bit upset or anxious, I have been practising visualising being in a calm, restful place. It doesn't always work but I feel I'm getting better with practice. In particular, I have found this helps me drift off more easily when I have a lot on my mind at night and I'm trying to go to sleep.

All-in-all, I am now confident in changing anxious images to calm imagery wherever I am. These are things that I did already. Now that I know they work I try and practise them more.

Step 4 Practise mindfulness

It is possible to use a technique called mindfulness to make a simple but significant change in the relationship of your thoughts, feelings and bodily sensations to the level of your stress. If you can see negative, stressful thoughts and feelings as everyday *events of the mind* rather than a deep essential part of your personality, you can use awareness exercises and mindfulness techniques to stop feelings of stress spiralling out of control and becoming a state of mind or chronic bad experience.

What is mindfulness?

It involves the following techniques, which can be practised and are both simple and can have a significant impact on our life:
- ✓ The ability to regularly be aware and listen to our thoughts, feelings and bodily sensations.
- ✓ The ability to be present-centred: staying in the here-and-now rather than the past or future.
- ✓ Acceptance and non-attachment to our thoughts and feelings as we experience them, whether they seem 'good' or 'bad'.
- ✓ Letting go of unhelpful cycles of introspection and self-analysis.
- ✓ 'Being' as a way of helping us to 'do': having a single focus at any one time can help us feel calm.

This has been practised for thousands of years, and has also been endorsed by many psychologists in the UK and USA in recent times.

In this step we will look at the following topics:
✓ Focus on your breathing.
✓ Choose productive thoughts.
✓ Appreciate your senses.
✓ Practise mindfulness meditation each day.
✓ Be more mindful all day.

Focus on your breathing

Just breathe.

What would you say to someone who is upset or panicking about something, perhaps after receiving some bad news?

You might say to them "relax – take a few deep breaths". This will usually help them calm down and feel more in control of their situation.

Breathing is something we can all do and focus on, from time to time, to feel calmer and at ease with ourselves and our environment.

Try sitting comfortably, closing your eyes and focussing your attention on your breathing in the following ways:
1) Slowly breathe in through your nose and fill up your lungs with air.
2) Then slowly exhale through your mouth.
3) Let your breathing flow in and out – try not to control it too much.
4) You can repeat this at least 5 times slowly or for a few minutes.

Just breathe. As you are doing this, allow your experience to be just that – an experience, without trying to manage or change or do something to it. If your mind wanders, gently bring your attention back to your breathing once again.

We can all learn to use our breath as an anchor to stay in the present and feel calm. It is a fundamental part of our life; the first experience of our life.

You can do it wherever you are:
- ✓ At home in bed.
- ✓ On the bus to work.
- ✓ Sitting at your desk.
- ✓ In the shopping queue.

It doesn't require any equipment, is something we can all do, doesn't take long and will help you feel more relaxed.

You can do it regularly throughout the day, everyday, however you are feeling. You can do it anytime, anywhere.

> James says:
> Sometimes I can find myself in bed unable to sleep, with lots on my mind. It's almost impossible to tell yourself to 'stop thinking about something', as it will only make you think about it more. What I find does work is taking and focussing on deep breaths. This takes my mind off what's worrying me and usually helps me to relax.... and slowly... drift... off...

Focus on your breathing: Sit comfortably now for a minute, breathe in slowly, exhale slowly and let your breathing flow. Try and concentrate only on your breathing. Does it help to relax you?

This week

Regularly, throughout each day, stop and focus on your breathing. Breathe in and out slowly and deeply to allow yourself to relax. You can do this whenever, wherever you are.

Choose productive thoughts

Your thoughts are mental events, not facts

What thoughts might you have **if you were looking out of your window at lunchtime on any normal day?** They could be something like:

> *"It looks nice out there.... I have a dry mouth.... I wish I could have done that differently... What am I doing tonight?... I feel great today....Will I have enough money to pay the gas bill this month?..."*

With practice we can train ourselves to be aware of thoughts, images or sensations, one at a time. **We often have a lot on our minds. Too many thoughts can confuse and overload us. Some negative thoughts make us stop and worry excessively (such as paying the gas bill in the above example).**

You don't need to hang onto your thoughts. **As thoughts arise, just focus your awareness on them as they pass through your mind. Treat them like your breathing – let them come in and pass away.**

You are bound to have some negative thoughts and images – **be aware of them with kind and gentle interest rather than anxiety and disappointment. Allow yourself some quiet reflection as to whether these thoughts are illogical, exaggerated, catastrophising, perfectionist or blaming.**

It's OK to pay more attention to one particular thought if it leads somewhere useful **and we can still feel calm. It's not OK if it makes us worried, stressed, tense *and* we don't do anything useful with it.**

To take this a stage further, **frequently pause and feel good about what is going on in your life and around you – feel contented and relaxed in this moment. Remember – even the little things in life can help you feel contented.**

With the example at the beginning of this topic, **where you are looking out of your window at lunchtime, you could pause and think about your morning, positively and with contentment. You might think:**

"It's been a good morning"; "I've done OK"; "The sun is out"; "I feel pretty healthy".

Focus more on productive and reassuring thoughts that can lead to positive feelings and actions.

Hugh says:
I get my fair share of negative or anxious worrying thoughts, but it helps to divert my brain from these on to something positive inside me (like a small job done well) or outside me (like the weather or the scene outside). It's all about perspective and not letting my worries take over.

Choose productive thoughts: Stop for a second now and let your thoughts flow. Practise only focussing on positive, logical and calm thoughts.

This week

Choose to let go of, and ignore, stressful, unproductive thoughts and focus only on calm, productive thoughts. Feel good about yourself, what you've been doing, your relationships and your day.

Appreciate your senses

See.... taste.... hear.... touch.... and smell....

We often miss 'the now'. We tend to think about the recent past (what's happened yesterday) and the approaching future (tomorrow's schedule).

We miss what we are feeling, seeing, touching, hearing and smelling at this present moment.

We are missing opportunities to feel relaxed and contented with all the amazing things that are happening all around us, all the time.

Practise focussing your senses on 'the now' wherever you are.

Ask yourself what you can sense. Practise making these sensations give you pleasure and make you feel calm.

Experience life from different viewpoints. Next time you go for a walk, whether in a town or the countryside, try and stay in the present moment; each step of the way appreciate what's going on around you.

Soak it all up. Enjoy the chill of the air or the warmth of the sun. Listen to the sounds of the birds flying above, the traffic, the people and the wind in the trees.

No two walks will ever be the same. No two moments will ever be the same. Learning to enjoy your senses can help you feel calmer, more positive and more alive.

James says:
If it's a fine day, I sometimes go for a short walk at lunchtime taking my lunch with me. I find a bench or some grass – somewhere to watch the world go by – and sit down to enjoy my food slowly. As I take in all the sights and sounds, I feel myself relax. You can do this whether you're at home or at work.

Appreciate your senses. What can you see, touch, hear, taste and smell right now? Enjoy these sensations for 30 seconds.

This week

Each day be more aware of, and enjoy each of your senses.

Practise mindfulness meditation each day

Feel calm and centred.

Over many hundreds and thousands of years, **people have talked about mindfulness meditation as a path to increased calmness.**

A world-renowned expert on mindfulness meditation is Jon Kabat-Zinn; one of his most famous books is called *'Full Catastrophe Living.'*

He has successfully helped people improve a range of illnesses as well as stress through mindfulness. Since the book was first published over 15 years ago, the practice of mindfulness meditation has spread to hospitals, medical centres and clinics throughout the world.

By combining some of the ideas from the previous topics, you can start to meditate.

Here's how you can get started:

1) Put aside 5–10 minutes a day to sit comfortably, quietly and uninterrupted.
2) Close your eyes and breathe in through your nose and out through your mouth, slowly.
3) Be aware of the movement of air in.... and.... out. Is it colder when you inhale than when you exhale?
4) Be aware of the physical sensations throughout your whole body, but don't dwell on them.
5) Let your thoughts pass through without concentrating too closely on any of them.
6) Bring your focus back to your breathing if your mind wanders from breathing and bodily sensations to other thoughts, issues and life dramas.

It's well worth reading *'Full Catastrophe Living'* if you wish to explore this topic further.

Mindfulness meditation is something you can do everyday to help you feel calm and centred.

It will take some practice and repeated use to really get the most out of it, but if you stay with it, it will be worth it.

> James says:
> I try each morning before breakfast to sit on my living room floor facing my window to meditate for 10 minutes. I find this is the best time for me, as my mind has not yet become busied with what I have to do in the day. I find that, when I do this, I start the day feeling calm, centred and contented.

Practise mindful meditation: **Put aside 5 minutes now or later today to sit somewhere quietly and without being interrupted. Close your eyes and focus on your breathing. Be aware of how relaxed and calm this makes you feel.**

This week

Put aside 5 minutes each day to practise mindful meditation. You may find it easier in the morning (when you have a clearer head) or in the evening (when you have more time). Experiment with both and see what works for you.

Be more mindful all day

Slow down, enjoy your day and remain calm.

All day, every day. Whatever you are doing, you can now begin to learn to be more mindful.

Anywhere. It can be while you walk somewhere, when you're on the bus, when you're in the shower, when you're sitting at home, when you're in the rain or when you're in a restaurant.

What you can do is:
- ✓ Focus on your **breathing** to help relax you.
- ✓ Appreciate all your different **senses.**
- ✓ Focus on your **positive, logical and calm thoughts**.
- ✓ Focus on what you are doing right now – **stay in the moment** and enjoy each sensation.
- ✓ Be aware of what **little things** give you a sense of satisfaction, achievement, mastery and control.

Slow down, enjoy it. As you pass through your day, try to remember to use these skills to help you remain calm.

Compliment yourself on what you have done. This fleeting congratulation gives you a well-earned bounce in your step, which will help propel you forwards.

Hugh says:
Whether I'm at work, at home, travelling or just out for a walk, I try to practise being mindful. It's a way of clearing my mind of the various stresses and strains we all have and, for a few moments, slowing down.

Be more mindful everyday: Focus now on where you are at this moment. Are you feeling calm and relaxed? Enjoy the moment.

This week

Be more mindful all day, every day. Be aware of the little things that make you feel good, and enjoy them.

Getting started on Step 4...

....Today, tomorrow and this week: Sit down somewhere quiet first thing in the morning and practise mindfulness meditation for 5 minutes. This will help you start your day feeling calm and collected. Throughout the day be more mindful of your senses and thoughts. Aim to appreciate moments in your day as much as possible and compliment yourself on the little things that you get done. Focus on productive, positive thoughts – how do they make you feel? Regularly take a second to take a few deep breaths to help relax you; you can do this wherever you are.

Omar

Omar

Previously, I have tended to think in a negative and anxious style. My mind would often dwell on apparently difficult things in the past, that day or anticipate a bad day to come. I found it hard to focus on the here and now, and be contented with that. Before, I would typically walk home on a beautiful sunny day and hardly have seen, smelled or heard anything on the journey due to being so preoccupied with negative thoughts. I know this because I have only just started to notice all the different sights, smells and sounds now....

I am making a real effort to focus more on the here and now and not get caught up thinking about my past or future. I've found that if I do get a bit worked up, I can calm myself down by focussing on my breathing. I can do this anywhere, anytime – when I'm on the train, having lunch, in a meeting or when I'm going for a walk – it makes me feel much calmer. I have also got into a regular routine of spending 5-10 minutes each morning doing a simple meditation exercise in my lounge. When I started, I wasn't sure if it was having any effect. The longer I have persisted with it, though, the calmer and more centred I have felt.

Throughout the day, I try to be aware of thoughts as they come into my brain but not dwell on them too much. The negative thoughts aren't 'me', they are just negative thoughts – so I try and let them pass through and focus on the positive ones. I have found that the more I spend time thinking about the good things each day, the better I feel and more motivated I am to achieve the goals I have set myself.

During lunch times I find a quiet spot to sit and eat my sandwich, nice and slowly. Even if it's busy and the weather is bad, I try to sit still and pay attention to all my senses. I know it sounds silly, but I find this really relaxing. It's definitely better than rushing around all lunchtime without the opportunity to take breath. On the way home after work, I practise looking, listening and smelling what's around me on route. I also allow myself to have contented thoughts about myself and the day I have just had.

Although I still find myself thinking negatively on occasions, I am more aware that I'm doing it and try and change these negative thoughts to positive ones. I now know what a big effect this has on how I feel.

Thinking Summary Illustration

Omar is now better at thinking to reduce stress - today is just like any other working day for Omar:

1) He wakes up

Omar thinks about his day ahead **optimistically**, 'Today is going to be a good day', he predicts. Making a **positive prediction** he adds, 'I am going to make it so'.

2) Morning meditation

Omar always makes time to **practise mindful meditation** for 5 minutes before work. He finds it helps to centre him, allowing him to start the day calmly.

3) Bus to work

It is busy and uncomfortable on the bus. 'It won't take long - at least I'm out of the rain!' Omar thinks **focussing on the positives**. Whilst on route he **visualises success** - getting things done today and doing them well.

4) Something goes wrong

Omar gets ticked off by his boss for a mistake he has made. 'Don't worry' he says to **reassure** himself, 'it could have happened to anybody'.

5) *Lunch break*

Being more mindful, Omar slowly eats his sandwich, enjoying each taste of every mouthful. Having finished, he **focusses on his breathing** and relaxes.

6) *Successful meeting*

Omar and his colleague have different views on how to proceed on a project. Omar puts his across in a calm manner **assertively expressing himself.** He then listens to his colleague with an **open mind.** They compromise; Omar is happy.

7) *The walk home*

As he walks home he **appreciates his senses** – listening to the birds sing, smelling the summer air and feeling the early evening sun warm his face. He thinks 'Well done - this has been a good day!' **recognising his everyday successes,** and smiles.

Summary Thinking to reduce stress

This section has looked into ways of feeling calmer through how you think. Positive thinking can be a huge help in remaining calm.

We suggest you hold back from starting the next section and allow yourself a week to try out and continue practising your *Thinking to reduce stress.*

We hope you have already completed each *AS* in this section. If not, complete any remaining ones as soon as you can. For the rest of the week, continue with the part marked *this week* .

Take the positives out of each new idea you try out.

Don't worry if you find certain topics difficult at first – reassure yourself that they are worthwhile and that you can do them.

Keep working at them, you'll soon get the hang of them.

Think positively

Be more confident.
Be more optimistic.
Focus on the positives.
Be assertive and express yourself.
Recognise your successes.
Reassure yourself if you make a mistake.
Identify, challenge and change negative thoughts.

Think logically

Be more specific, exaggerate less.
Make positive predictions, don't catastrophise.
Face up to facts.
Accept yourself: you are what you are and that's OK.
Use problem-solving techniques.
Understand other people's actions.
Learn not to overreact emotionally.
Distract yourself from anxious thoughts.
Question your beliefs with an open mind.
Identify, challenge and change illogical thoughts.

Imagine calmness

Use calm imagery to relax you.
Visualise success in everything you do.
Use motivation imagery to encourage you to achieve your goals.

Practise mindfulness

Focus on your breathing.
Focus on productive thoughts.
Appreciate your senses.
Practise mindful meditation every day.
Be more mindful all day.

Take a week to continue practising these ideas. It will then be time to look at *Lifestyle to reduce stress*.

Section 3 Lifestyle to reduce stress

Our lifestyle can become a force of habit, which we repeat day in, day out, without paying it too much thought.

This can either be a positive lifestyle routine which helps us feel healthy, happy and calm. Or it can be a negative lifestyle routine which contributes to us feeling unhealthy, unhappy and stressed.

The good news is that whatever your lifestyle is now – you can make small, positive changes from *today* that will give you immediate benefits.

This section shows you how:
- ✓ Being active is both an instant and long-term de-stressor.
- ✓ Eating, drinking and smoking can all affect your calmness.
- ✓ Your home is your calm castle.
- ✓ A balanced lifestyle helps you feel more in control.

Approach this section, as with others, with an open mind.

If you don't think the Active Steps (*AS*) can help you feel calmer – try them out anyway as you may be pleasantly surprised.

If you don't think you've got the time – make the time to at least try out some of the *AS* from each step.

If you don't think you will be able to do them – you can, they are all within your reach.

Making small changes to your lifestyle will make a big difference to your feelings of calmness and well-being.

Jack

Jack has been suffering from stress recently. He has identified that his poor lifestyle may be part of the problem.

I am 24, single and work in a bar in Town. I live in a shared flat with 3 male friends. Recently I found myself becoming more aware that I had a fairly unhealthy lifestyle. My diet, drinking, smoking and lack of exercise were all beginning to contribute to me feeling unfit, unhealthy and generally stressed.

I found it difficult to balance out my time between working, socialising with my friends and time for myself. The balance was tipping too far towards unhealthy activities. This needed to change. Over the past few years I had developed a regular eating routine which was easy. I had never really enjoyed cooking and would generally go for ready meals, take-outs or eat at the pub. Eating was usually rushed. Whether at home or out-on-the-town, midweek or on the weekend – I was a regular drinker. I didn't monitor what or how much alcohol I would have, but liked the feeling of relaxation I got after my 4th or 5th drink. I would look forward to that feeling as I got on with my day. Like most of my friends, I smoked.

I wasn't at all into exercise. A long time ago, I used to play football but I'd stopped, and I'd forgotten what being fit felt like. I wasn't obese but could have done with losing a few pounds. Even though I would pretend to be 'happy' to be unfit to my friends, really I wanted to look and feel a bit different. When I looked in the mirror I didn't feel particularly attractive or self-confident. I just wasn't sure how I could change this.

Apart from my work and socialising, I had few, if any hobbies. I've always been interested in lots of different stuff but hadn't got into anything and stuck to it. I never thought I had the time or that there was any point. That said, I saw other people doing things and wondered what it must be like to have a hobby you're passionate about, outside of the pub! I began to feel that I had started to let myself go. In fact it had probably been going on for a while. I was tired of waking up in the morning and getting home at the end of the day to my flat – it was a real mess. I was tired too of doing the same things each day. I was also tired of *feeling* tired and unfit.

Step 5 Get active

It's never too late to start a more energetic lifestyle, and by getting more active you can enjoy both instant and long-term improvements to your mind and body.

Going for a brisk walk or jog is a great way to de-stress yourself if you're having a difficult day.

It is important that, in approaching a more active lifestyle, you ease yourself in slowly and allow your body to adjust to the increased demands you are placing on it.

If you have had any health scares or problems, or are over the age of 50, consult a doctor before attempting anything too strenuous.

Set yourself small and realistic targets so you feel reinforced in hitting them.

Through this step we want you to experiment with the following topics:
- ✓ Visualise the benefits.
- ✓ Have an active lifestyle.
- ✓ Enjoy regular exercise.
- ✓ Try relaxation exercise.
- ✓ Set goals: enjoy it.
- ✓ Activate your mind: be creative.

Visualise the benefits

What would having more exercise mean to you?

Physical and mental benefits. Increasing the amount of exercise you take will give you many benefits. These benefits will help you feel more in control of your personal stress levels.

Set up a positive cycle of increased mood and stress reduction through increasing your activity levels:
- ✓ Burn up daily stressful adrenalin.
- ✓ Anger management.
- ✓ Increase resting metabolic rate.
- ✓ Weight control.
- ✓ Release of feel-good endorphins.
- ✓ Sense of achievement.
- ✓ Enhancement of self-esteem.
- ✓ Improved work performance.
- ✓ Reduce cholesterol levels.

Imagine. How would it feel to experience these benefits – do you think it would help you feel calmer?

Do. Could you do a little bit more regular exercise in order to enjoy more of the above benefits?

Feel. If you did 5 minutes extra exercise today, how do you think you would feel afterwards?

Hugh says:
I actually enjoy going for a run or a cycle, although I should do this more often. One way to feel like doing more is for me to imagine jogging around the park near where I live. Thinking about how it would feel during and after makes it more likely I will do it when I have time.

Visualise enjoying the benefits of getting active: **Stop and visualise yourself enjoying each of the benefits in the above list.** Below, pick the two benefits that you would most like to experience more and more.

The two benefits of being active that I would most like to experience are:

1) ....

2) ....

This week

Visualise the two benefits you have written down every time you go for a walk or do any other form of exercise.

Have an active lifestyle

Choose the active option.

Take a more energetic option to get from A to B. The first thing for you to do is increase your general activity levels. Soon this will become second nature and you will enjoy the extra activity, and the way it makes you feel.

Why not:
- ✓ Walk instead of drive to the shops.
- ✓ Cycle to work.
- ✓ Walk briskly between offices or office buildings.
- ✓ Use the stairs instead of the lift.
- ✓ Go for a stroll before bedtime.
- ✓ Go for a long walk each weekend.
- ✓ Spend an hour gardening each week.
- ✓ Spend more time playing energetically with your children in the garden or park.
- ✓ Watch less TV in the evenings and do something more active.

The more activity you do, the more energy you will have. You may feel that you already live an active enough lifestyle or that you don't have enough time or energy to be more active. You will find, though, that activity energises you. You'll feel good for it, too.

Any extra activity all adds up; every cycle to the shops to get some bread, every walk to work and every playtime in the park.

Weekly routine. Think now how you could get more active as part of your weekly routine. You can plan to build in more activity into your evenings and your weekends if that helps make it happen.

Choose the active option more. You also face frequent decisions of whether to get somewhere by being active or by taking the car, bus or taxi – which is less active. Start choosing the active option more, when possible.

Fill unexpected gaps in your day with a quick walk around the block to stretch your legs and get some air. Try and appreciate the benefits of a quick 5 minutes burst of exercise – this starts the ball rolling to more regular activity.

Experiment: see how active a lifestyle you can lead and how this makes you feel. Even if you make one extra active choice each day, it will help you feel calmer and happier.

James says:
I don't own a bicycle, but I try to walk to places whenever I can. When I know I need to go somewhere, I always first ask myself whether it is possible for me to walk there, before considering driving. I have found that I'm prepared to walk further and further now, especially at weekends. I enjoy the exercise, fresh air and appreciating my senses as I go. It feels freer than being in a car, especially if the traffic is bad. I often take my camera with me too, just in case I see something interesting along the way.

14th August	Personal Calmness Bank 1027

14th August
DATE

"*Pay me...15 Minutes...exercise*"   £ *15.00*

C. Taylor

2222222 : 000 111 555 1027

AS

Have an active lifestyle: Go for a walk today or cycle to work, to the shops or to meet people. It doesn't matter if it is only a small distance, or for just a few minutes.

I am going to get the following exercise today:

....

This is when I am going to do it:

....

This week

Plan for at least one extra piece of activity a day compared to what you do at the moment. When and where can you do this? First thing in the morning to get the paper? To get to work? A walk round the block on your lunch break? A mid-afternoon stroll to the park? An evening cycle ride?

Enjoy regular exercise

Get your heart rate up.

In addition to your more active day-to-day lifestyle, try some regular exercise. There is lots that you can do so choose something which is suitable for you and which you will enjoy:

Home exercise
- ✓ Walking, jogging, running, rowing – outdoors or on a machine at home.
- ✓ Repetitive exercise can be **calming**. Breathe rhythmically and deeply.
- ✓ Have a set of **dumb-bells** at home.
- ✓ Use your own **body-weight** (press-ups and sit-ups).
- ✓ If short on time – get up 15 minutes earlier in the **morning** and go for a run.
- ✓ Or go for a relaxing, mindful walk **before bedtime**.

Gym membership
- ✓ For a **range of equipment** – cardio-vascular and resistance.
- ✓ Often have organised exercise **classes** you can take part in.
- ✓ Many have **swimming pools, squash and tennis courts**.
- ✓ Can seek advice from well-trained **personal trainers**.
- ✓ Find one which is **best for you**: a convenient location, affordable and that has the right feel and equipment.

Team sport
- ✓ A sociable way to get fitter.
- ✓ Re-visit a sport you may have **played before** but have given up.
- ✓ Start **something fresh** and interesting.
- ✓ Get the **buzz** of competitive sport and make new friends.

Do you fancy exercising from home? It's easy to get started – all you need is a pair of trainers, some comfortable clothing and 30 minutes to go for a quick walk or run. This is inexpensive and can fit into your schedule for convenience. Train on your own or with a training partner to help motivate you.

Would you enjoy becoming a member of a local gym? There will probably be several in your area and they offer different deals depending on your age and intended usage. Pop in and speak to somebody face to face, tell them what you are looking to get out of it and have a good look around. You should be able to speak to a personal trainer to discuss putting together your own personal workout plan too. Doing this may mean a financial sacrifice – like cutting down on alcohol or your eating-out budget each week. If it means you get fitter and feel all the better for it, though, it could be worth it.

Interested in playing some sport? You can find out about local team sports and clubs through the internet or local papers. You could always go along with a friend or relative for a bit of moral support and to make it even more fun.

Hugh says:
Because of my schedule, the best time for me to train in the week is in the morning. Twice a week, I get up at 6am and do a 30 minute run or cycle around a nearby park. I find that this always sets me up for a good day – I feel energised, alert and motivated once I have finished. Breakfast always tastes better too!

Enjoy regular exercise: What form of regular exercise suits you best – home exercise, gym membership or team sport? Write this down below, being as specific as you can as to what you will be doing.

I am going to start/continue to enjoy the following regular exercise:

....

This week

Get started. If you plan to exercise from home, go for at least one run, cycle or workout. If you are going to join a gym, research the different options, find the best one, join up and have a work out. If you are already a member somewhere, that's great – get yourself down there for at least one good workout. If you are going to get involved with a team sport, research your options and get in contact. If it is out of season or they have nothing on this week – exercise from home until they do.

Try relaxation exercise

Meditation in motion.

Pilates, Yoga or Tai Chi. If you wish to practise a more relaxing form of exercise, why not try one of these ancient eastern arts? They have been around for thousands of years and are still popular today.

Try them to:
- ✓ Develop **mindfulness**.
- ✓ Develop **body awareness**.
- ✓ Bring on the **relaxation response**.
- ✓ Increase **flexibility**.
- ✓ Increase **co-ordination**.
- ✓ Improve **weight control**.

You can either practise:
- ✓ At home.
- ✓ In a group.
- ✓ With a private instructor.

Research the information on each of these online or in a bookshop.

Find out more about what groups are in your area through your local paper, newsagent or gym.

Take relaxation exercise: Try to find out about some of these activities online or in a bookshop. Have a look today in your local paper or newsagent's window and see what local classes there are in something like Pilates, Yoga or Tai Chi. If you see something of interest, write down the number and the address.

This week

Call them up or pop in to see what it's about. They will be pleased to see you, make you feel welcome and explain a little more about the different classes they run from beginner to more advanced.

Set goals: enjoy it

What's your goal?

Motivation. Some people find having an exercise goal is a great way to motivate them.

Visualisation. Picturing achieving your goal can push you forwards.

Why have a goal? This could be to:
- ✓ Help you train even when you don't want to (like when it's raining).
- ✓ Push you harder when you feel like stopping.
- ✓ Feel an even greater sense of achievement when you finish.

What goal? A positive goal could be to:
- ✓ Reduce weight.
- ✓ Reduce body fat.
- ✓ Reduce waist size.
- ✓ Improve on distances or times.
- ✓ Train for a race or event.
- ✓ Raise money for charity.

Whatever it is that you are doing, enjoy it! After all, you have many options available to you, so try to choose some form of activity that makes you happy.

Think positively about your exercise routine. If you approach it with enthusiasm, you are more likely to enjoy it and get the most out of it.

Find out what works for you. Some people prefer training alone, some with a friend, others in a group. There are no rules so experiment and once you have found something that works for you, there will be no stopping you.

Routine. Getting into a regular routine of roughly set times and set days for certain activities can help you manage your time more efficiently and ensure you don't miss out on your weekly quota of getting active.

Hugh says:
At the age of 56, I recently started competing in sprint triathlons.
I found it gave me the focus I needed to get up early in the morning
and push myself. Although they are hard work, I enjoy the races,
especially finishing them, and have managed to raise some money for
good causes too.

Set yourself goals and think positively about being active: **Set yourself one
goal now to help motivate you to increase your activity levels.**

My goal for getting active is:

....

This week

Remind yourself of this goal as often as you can and use it to help
motivate you to increase your activity levels. Whenever you exercise,
think positively about yourself and what you are doing. Enjoy the feeling
of healthy tiredness you experience once you've finished, too!

Activate your mind: be creative

The mind has a limitless ability to create and be creative.

Make time. Just as it's important to take regular exercise, make time to be creative, too. Although some people get the chance to think creatively at work, the more time you spend on your own creative pursuits the better for your own personal stress relief.

Investing some time into one, or a number of, creative pursuits can help in a number of ways:
- ✓ **Distract yourself** – from other stressful thoughts or events that may be preoccupying your mind.
- ✓ **Find like-minded people** – who share your creative passion and who you can spend time and discuss ideas with.
- ✓ **Help you feel alive** – get outside your comfort zone and challenge yourself.
- ✓ **Uncover new creative talent** – the brain's imagination and creativity is endless. The more creative you are, the more creative you become.
- ✓ **Increase your self-confidence** – surprise yourself with what you can achieve and have something to show for it.

Old or new. It could be something that you started at school but gave up for one reason or another, or something completely fresh that you've always wanted to start but never thought you had the ability or time.

How about:
- ✓ **Reading** more.
- ✓ **Drawing.**
- ✓ **Painting.**
- ✓ Playing a **musical instrument.**
- ✓ **Photography.**
- ✓ **Home improvement** or carpentry.
- ✓ **Gardening.**
- ✓ **Pottery.**
- ✓ **Writing** (poetry, a book, songs).

✓ Brainstorming (ideas, plans, projects).
✓ Keeping a diary or journal.

The key is to get started and then planning, and spending some time each week creatively. Turn the TV off for a while in the evening and give something a go.

For yourself, for others. Your creative pursuit can be something personal but can also be something you can do to share with others. You could paint a picture for someone. You could write a poem or limerick. You could jam with your friends once a week to get more out of playing your musical instrument.

Stick at it. The more time you spend working at something the better you will get. It starts with the 'first five minutes'.

Creativity breeds creativity. The more time you spend being creative the more creative you will become, and the more rewarding it will be.

James says:
If you like taking photographs, here's a gift idea. Find a shot that you think someone will like and an interesting frame from a charity shop. Get the photo printed at your local processors (they will help you edit it if necessary). Put it in the frame. Wrap it. There you have it – an original, inexpensive and thoughtful gift.

Do something creative: Decide on one creative pursuit you would like to do more of each week. Write this down below:

A creative pursuit I would like to do more of is:

....

This week

Get yourself any equipment which you need to begin. From there, make yourself the time to spend at least an hour during the week getting started or continuing with your hobby.

_____

Getting started on Step 5...

...Today, tomorrow and this week: Experiment with being as 'active' and 'creative' as you can. Get out and about on foot or by cycle wherever possible. If you can't make journeys in this way, just go for a short walk around the block first thing in the morning, at lunch and/or in the evening. Try to also fit a more strenuous walk, run or cycle into your day or even a trip down to the local gym. Ease yourself in, and think positively about the exercise you are taking; visualise all the worthwhile benefits you will gain. Are you interested in a form of relaxation exercise? Do some research, and if possible, investigate where and when you can start. Don't forget your creative side! Spend some time getting started or continuing with a creative pursuit that takes your interest.

How does all this activity make you feel? Relaxed? Happy? Satisfied? Energised? Calm? If you have enjoyed becoming more active physically and creatively this week, carry on with the active and creative activities you have started.

Jack

Jack

I had got to the point where I was feeling unfit, unhealthy and stressed out much of the time. Apart from working, eating and drinking, I had no other hobbies and lived a fairly static lifestyle. I realised that I needed to make some changes. Over the last couple of months I've gradually been getting more active.

The first thing I did was start to walk to the bar. The 2 mile walk takes about 20-25 minutes. It feels good stretching my legs and getting some fresh air. I enjoy taking in the sights. There's always something going on: interesting people, the traffic, wildlife and the changing skies above. Walking has really helped me to relax – both the process and the results. On my day off, I have started to pick a place of interest in my area and walk there. I recently started to use a pedometer to measure how far I walked and was amazed to find I was walking 30-35 miles a week. I now set a weekly target of walking 10% more than the previous week – this target motivates me to walk further. I'm enjoying the challenge.

At home, I have started to cut down on how much TV I watch. Instead I try to get on with some jobs in the flat or to get out of the flat altogether. Although sometimes it's great just to sit down and chill out, I'm beginning to enjoy the feeling of being up and about more and more. It all adds to the miles too.

I have decided to join a gym next. I want to start swimming and doing a few light weights for a bit of variation from the walks. The local gym is offering a good deal for new people joining so this would suit me. I'm excited about getting started!

All this activity is making me feel healthier, more alert and is also boosting my self-confidence. I feel more motivated, not only to get fitter but also to challenge myself in other areas of my life. I have recently joined a photography club which meets every Tuesday evening. I'm learning how to take better shots and am really enjoying having something creative to focus on. I'm enjoying meeting new people too. Now, whenever I've got some time to myself, I go out walking around town with my camera around my neck and my pedometer on my side. The photography course has given me a different view of the city in which I live. I feel that being more active has given me a new lease of life.

Step 6 Eat and drink healthily

Some common habits people use to cope with stress include eating unhealthily, smoking and drinking. These habits reduce your health and well-being in the long run and can increase your feelings of stress and lack of control. What you eat and drink affects your weight and your general health, both of which affect your stress levels.

A positive diet will help prevent you getting ill with colds, coughs and sicknesses. It will help you feel more energised, alert and motivated. It will help you become more active, sleep better and look and feel well.

We do not want to stop you enjoying eating and drinking, and certainly do not advise you go on any crash diet. However, we do want to give you some good pointers towards getting into a regular weekly routine of healthier eating and drinking – both in terms of what and how you eat.

We will discuss later in this step the need for you to be careful if you are smoking or drinking to alleviate feelings of stress. There are many issues involved, such as dependency and long-term health.

Please read these topics at the end of this step with an open mind – it is up to you what you decide to do.

By putting into practice the topics in this step, in combination with getting more active (Step 5), you will feel better physically and emotionally.

In this step we will look at these topics:
- ✓ Eat regularly.
- ✓ Enjoy more home cooking.
- ✓ Reduce unhealthy foods: 'The red list'.
- ✓ Increase healthy foods: 'The green list'.
- ✓ Eat slowly: eat less.
- ✓ Apply the 80:20 principle.
- ✓ Smoking.
- ✓ Alcohol.

Eat regularly

Keep your metabolism fired up.

Why might you miss a meal?
- ✓ **Running late.** Because you are late for work in the morning.
- ✓ **Too busy.** Because you are too busy at home or work for lunch.
- ✓ **Money.** Because you don't have the right money.

There are a couple of really good reasons for you not to miss meals:

1) Craving and over-indulging – You are more at risk of your good intentions going out the window the hungrier you are. It's easy to think either 'I deserve this because I didn't eat breakfast' or 'I'm so hungry I just don't care!' as you stroll into a fast-food chain with a rumbling stomach. It can get to a point where you feel you've just got to eat, no matter what it is.

2) Your metabolism – Your metabolism is what burns up what you eat and turns it into energy. A fast metabolism keeps you feeling energised and helps prevent too much food turning into fat. A slow metabolism

can have the opposite effect. When you regularly miss meals, your body's metabolism can slow down so that you are not burning up the food you are eating. Effectively, because you're not eating regularly, your body is saying, 'I'm not sure where my next meal's coming from – I'd better store up what is eaten just in case I don't get supplied again for a while'. Your body will start storing as fat more of what you *do* eat.

How can you stop yourself from missing meals?

1) Have three nutritious meals each and every day – Have breakfast, lunch and supper every day to keep your metabolism fired up, body energised and mind alert. Go for foods from 'the green list' and reduce items from 'the red list' more and more (see later in this step). This isn't a licence to over-eat. Eat slowly and stop when or just before you are full.

2) Have two 'mid-snacks' each and every day – Mid-morning (or about halfway between breakfast and lunch) and mid-afternoon (or about halfway between lunch and supper) have a quick snack. Go for healthy, portable 'fast-food' such as a small packet of unsalted nuts, a piece of fruit/vegetable or yoghurt. These snacks will help keep you going through to your next meal. If you are well-prepared or have easy access to healthy snacks at work, mid-snacking doesn't have to take up much valuable work time.

3) Plan your three meals and two mid-snacks – This is a key part to making this happen, as with lots of other areas in this book. If you have had problems with missing meals in the past, or are not used to having a nutritious 'mid-snack' – good planning will help you to remember. As much as possible, prepare each of your 5 meals yourself. If you are working, you should still have time in the evening to prepare lunch and two snacks for the next day so that all you need to do is get up and have a good breakfast. Have a supply of nutritious food and drink at home.

4) Do it with a partner, friend or colleague – Talk about this topic with your partner and friends. Sometimes it can help to give things a go with someone else.

AS

Eat regularly: Have three nutritious meals and two mid-snacks today or tomorrow. What will you have?

....

Breakfast

....

Mid-snack

....

Lunch

....

Mid-snack

....

Supper

This week

Eat regularly each day. Plan what main meals you will have and have a supply of healthy mid-snacks in the house.

Enjoy more home cooking

There are many benefits to enjoying more home cooking.

We all enjoy eating out. This could be a burger and fries, a Chinese take-away or at a sit-down restaurant.

Sometimes you may feel too tired to cook, or have no food at home. You may be in a rush or too hungry to say no. Or you may just be enjoying eating out socially or celebrating something.

Eating out too often can mean eating more unhealthy food choices and over-eating. Of course, this is not *always* the case, but it is *often* the case. It can contribute to you spending more money than you would like, drinking more, becoming more inactive and feeling unhealthy.

Increasing your home cooking can result in a number of benefits:

1) Stay more in control of what you eat – Every meal you prepare yourself can be healthier if you are sensible with quantities and mainly use ingredients from 'the green list'.
2) Enjoy the benefits of a better diet – The more you are preparing your own meals, the better your eating routine will be, the better you will feel and the more you will feel motivated to stick to eating regularly and well.
3) Save some money – Preparing food from home can be cheaper than the cheapest of fast foods, so save yourself some money.
4) Really enjoy eating out – If you manage to reduce the amount you are eating out, and are eating healthily from home instead, when you do go out you can really treat yourself, guilt free, to whatever you want!

Here are a few practical ideas to help you cut-down on eating out and increase home cooking:

1) Plan ahead – As much as possible, plan what meals you are going to have at the start of the week. This will allow you to do a weekly shop.
2) Do a weekly shop – It's a great idea to get in a weekly food shop. This means you have plenty of supplies to hand for whatever healthy meal or snack you want all week. It can also be a much more cost-effective way of shopping.
3) Use online recipes – If you're looking for some inspiration for your cooking, there are lots of brilliant quick and easy recipes you can find for free at www.bbc.co.uk/food
4) Cook extra and freeze – When you are cooking evening meals, why not cook an extra amount and freeze it? It will keep for at least a month and will offer you a quick and healthy alternative to a take-away when you can't face cooking.
5) Share cooking duties – If possible, share the cooking with the people you live with whether it be partner, family or friends.
6) Prepare packed lunches/mid-snacks the night before – This means everything is prepared and out of the way.

Target. Try to set your own target for reducing the amount you eat out from now on.

Halve. Work out how often, on average, you eat-out on average a week, and cut this in half – preparing meals at home instead.

Savings. You still get to eat out a bit and you'll really appreciate the savings and health benefits.

James says:
I do like a good curry, especially on a Sunday night for some reason! I try to alternate between eating out/take-aways and cooking my own meals at home. It saves me money, is healthier and I get to learn new recipes along the way.

Enjoy more home cooking: Work out how many times you ate out for breakfast, lunch or supper last week.

The number of times I ate out last week:

....

This week

Aim to reduce this number by half, enjoying more home cooking instead. Plan what meals you will have each day using this step to help you.

Reduce unhealthy foods: 'The red list'

Understand more about the food you eat.

Fight off stress. Understanding more about the food we eat and making good dietary decisions allows us to fight off stress, but is also good for our general health and long-term well-being.

Long-term changes. The trick is not to go for quick-fix diets, but to make gradual long-term changes to your general eating habits.

As a 'rule of thumb' doing the following will help you reduce unhealthy foods in your diet:
Move away from man-made foods such as refined sugars, refined fats and simple white carbohydrates (such as white bread and white pasta). These have little (if any) nutritional value.

Steer clear of ready-made or canned foods, as they tend to be nutritionally poor *and* are high in sugar and salt. Too much salt can lead to high blood pressure and an increased risk of heart disease and strokes.

Monitor your caffeine intake. Although caffeine can help keep you awake and alert due to its being a stimulant, drinking too much can leave you feeling anxious and irritable. Many people can handle lots of caffeine without encountering any side effects, but if you are *already* feeling anxious or stressed, caffeine is likely to make this feeling worse, not better. Try slowly reducing your intake of caffeine to avoid withdrawal – gradually cutting out caffeinated fizzy drinks and switching to decaffeinated tea and coffee.

Go easy on the alcohol. In contrast to caffeine, alcohol is a depressant, which can help to relax you. It is easy to become reliant on alcohol as a 'quick fix' to deal with a stressful occurrence or day. Remember that drinking heavily will have negative consequences for your sleep patterns, your general health, your bank balance and productivity. Experiment with other ways to help you to relax such as mindful meditation, instant relaxation (see p201), a walk or a run, or phoning a friend. We look at alcohol in more detail later in this step.

'The red list' includes:
Refined sugars - sweets; fizzy drinks; ice cream; jams/preserves; canned food; carton juices; ready meals.
Refined grains - white rice, white bread and white pasta which have most of their goodness removed.
Refined fats - fast food; baked goods; cakes; crisps; ready meals; fried food other than with olive oil.
Full fat dairy - cheese; milk; yoghurt.
Salt - canned food; crisps; ready meals; salted nuts.
Caffeine - coffee; tea; some fizzy/energy drinks, chocolate, pain-killers.
Alcohol

Hugh says:
I do a lot of driving on the motorway. I used to stop regularly for crisps and coffee, which did little for my weight or blood pressure. I now go for fruit, a light sandwich and water or juice. I save a coffee for when I'm feeling tired.

AS

Reduce your intake from 'the red list' from today. Which three of the above items could you reduce? Write these down below:

I could reduce the following three 'red list' items from my diet:

....

....

....

This week

Reduce the items you have written above in your diet.

Increase healthy foods: 'The green list'

Health has many sides to it.

It is important to remember that a healthy diet can help us be more relaxed and at ease.

How can I increase the healthy foods in my diet?
Move towards fresh 'whole foods' that contain unaltered natural goodness.

For your daily dose of vitamins and anti-oxidants, fruit and vegetables are crammed full. Avocados even contain protein and healthy fats.

For fibre, vitamins and minerals, wholegrain breads, pastas and rice are far superior to their white counterparts.

To get good quality protein in your diet, eat more lean white meat (less fatty than beef and pork). Omega-3 oils are good for the heart and joints. These can be found in oily fish such as tuna, mackerel and salmon.

What is 'the green list'?
Fruits & vegetables - eat a varied selection; raw or lightly cooked to maximise nutrients.
Lean protein - fish; white meats such as chicken and turkey; white cheese; beans and lentils; low fat live yoghurt.
Wholegrain carbohydrates - pasta; bread; rice; wild and basmati rice; non-fried potatoes.
Healthy fats - olive oil; avocado; non salted/roasted nuts; oily fish.
Water - tap or bottled; drink at least 2 litres a day – more if exercising.

Making small changes to your diet can help your general health and stress levels in the following ways:
Toxins. Clear your body of toxins.
Weight. Lose some excess weight.
Energy. Feel brighter and more energetic.
Long-term. Improvements to your long-term health.

Try a 7-14 day experiment. Stick as closely as possible to items on 'the green list' whilst cutting down on items on 'the red list'. You will find that your taste buds start to change, which will help you to enjoy the 'green list' foods more.

Start with your next meal. See for yourself how good you feel afterwards. We hope you'll feel like incorporating some of the changes into your regular diet.

James says:
I like the way eating healthily during the week helps me feel. It sounds obvious, but it definitely helps having healthy options at home and not having cupboards and fridges stacked up with chocolate, biscuits and crisps. I find that if it's there – I'll eat it!

Increase your intake from 'the green list' from today: Which three of the above 'green list' items will you increase in your diet? Write them down below:

I will increase the following three 'green list' items in my diet:

....

....

....

This week

Plan a weekly shop from 'the green list' so that you can enjoy more healthy home cooking and so that you shop more efficiently.

Eat slowly: eat less

Enjoy each and every mouthful.

Eat to live. Some people live to eat rather than eat to live, wanting a feeling of fullness by racing through their meal as quickly as possible.

Take things a little slower. This is also an indication of the modern day rush - always needing to get somewhere soon, which can make it difficult to stop and enjoy taking things slower, such as our food.

What's wrong with rushing our food?
Not knowing when you're full – It takes a little time for the message to get from your stomach to your brain. If we are literally 'stuffing our faces', we may have had an extra half a plate by the time we realise it is time to stop!

Not realising what we're eating – We are not allowing ourselves the time to contemplate what we are eating. This can make it easier for us to develop bad eating habits.

Not good for digestion – Swallowing half-chewed pieces of meat and bread is not helping the digestive process. It leads to poorer digestion of whatever nutrients there are and other irregularities such as indigestion and constipation.

Unsociable – If you are eating as fast as possible, you are probably not leaving much room for conversation!

How can I eat a bit slower?
Eat slowly and relax – Take time to eat your meal. Use the time to enjoy the food, company and opportunity to relax. See it as time at home or at work to recharge your batteries.

Enjoy each mouthful – Get to know the different flavours and the textures in your mouth and appreciate them fully. The more you do so, and also eat nutritious foods, the more your taste buds will start to change.

Eat less – Try eating from a smaller plate and don't fill yourself *up to the brim*. Try not to go back for seconds. Leave room for a piece of fruit at the end of the meal.

Enjoy good company – If you are in somebody's company, be sociable and talk about what you and they have been doing. It's good to talk!

Hugh says:
Like most people, I enjoy eating. To try to stop myself eating too quickly, I put down my knife and fork after taking a mouthful to allow myself time to enjoy it before taking another mouthful.

Enjoy each and every mouthful: Stop now for a piece of fruit or a drink. Make a point of eating or drinking.... very.... slowly.... and.... mindfully. Enjoy each and every mouthful – all its flavours and textures.

This week

Eat your food slowly - take your time. Enjoy each and every mouthful of every meal. When eating a meal, put down your knife and fork between mouthfuls to help you enjoy it.

Apply the 80:20 principle

You don't need to miss out on your favourite food.

Food choices. We have already looked into what foods help provide a healthy, balanced diet and in turn help you feel calm (and the ones that do not).

Not all or nothing. This is not to say, however, that one burger or chocolate bar every now and then is a problem. In fact, feeling constant pressure to eat certain foods and avoid others is no good if you feel you are constantly 'missing out' on your favourite treats.

Try 80:20. A good way to tackle this is to use the 80:20 approach. This means that you should try and balance out your diet 80% from 'the green list' and 20% from 'the red list'.

Cheat day. You could allow yourself a 'cheat day' at the weekend or just spread the 20% out over the week. This way you don't feel that you are missing out too much and you still have a nicely balanced diet.

Taste buds change. You may find that your taste buds change anyway, and that you want less of the fatty, sugary, salty foods. That's fine – you can have less than the 20% if you wish.

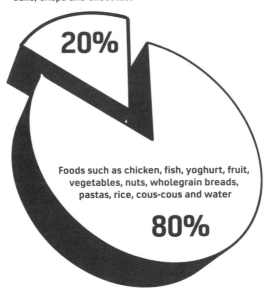

Foods such as sweets, fizzy drinks, canned food, ready meals, white carbs, fast food burger, indian take-away, cake, crisps and chocolate

20%

Foods such as chicken, fish, yoghurt, fruit, vegetables, nuts, wholegrain breads, pastas, rice, cous-cous and water

80%

James says:
I try to eat as healthily as I can during the week. It's when I take most of my exercise too. Come the weekend, I relax more and eat pretty much what I like.

Apply the 80:20 principle to your eating. Will you do this with a 'cheat day' (if so, on which day?) or by spreading the 20% out over the week?

I will apply the 80:20 principle by:

....

This week

Apply the 80:20 principle to your eating. Aim for 80% of your intake to come from 'the green list', with the other 20% from 'the red list'.

Smoking

Is the easier option always the best one?

For smokers only. If you are a non-smoker you can skip this and go to the start of the next topic. If you do smoke, read on: this is an important topic for you to consider.

50,000 people gave up smoking in 2007 (20% up on 2006). One of the authors of this book has successfully stopped smoking after 10 years, so we are aware what it's like to smoke, try and give up and enjoy life as a non-smoker. It is possible to successfully stop.

Consider your personal choice. Smoking is a personal choice. But, as someone who is looking for ways to feel calmer, you should at least consider that smoking may be contributing to your stress *more* than it is alleviating it.

Faulty assumptions. As a smoker you are constantly bombarded with reasons to give up. Some are self-generated, others from friends and family; others still from the government and health agencies. Deep down, every smoker knows of some good reasons why they should give up, and probably wants to as well. And the reasons some smokers do not give up are actually due to a number of faulty assumptions that they hold on to.

Self-inflicted stress. One of the most common misconceptions is that smoking *reduces* stress and makes you more relaxed. Where would you be without a cigarette to calm your nerves? But this is a trick of nicotine addiction. The withdrawal of nicotine is creating the very stress from which the next cigarette will 'relieve you'. You are relaxing yourself from a *self-inflicted stress*, which will keep on returning until the day you give up.

This is good news. What we are saying is that you can reduce a tangible amount of the feeling of stress in your life by *stopping smoking*.

There are other good reasons to give up too. Some to consider are:
- Your short-term health and fitness.
- To save money.
- Smoker's bad breath.
- Lethargy.
- Your taste-buds.
- Your family and friends.
- Your long-term health and future.
- It doesn't even taste good, anyway!

Your own list. If you are honest with yourself, you will probably have a list as long as your arm of reasons why *you* want to give up, compared with a very short one of reasons to continue.

Contributing to your stress. Think hard whether you want to carry on smoking. Consider that smoking is not only very bad for you and the people around you, but is contributing to, not solving, your feelings of stress.

Never regret stopping. It will take willpower to stop, but you can do it and once you do, you'll never regret it.

The free NHS smoking helpline is: 0800 022 4 332.

James says:

3 tips to help you stop that helped me:

1) Replace your 'after meal' or 'in car' cigarette with sugar free chewing gum.

2) Avoid some of the places where you used to smoke and some of the people you used to smoke with.

3) Increase your exercise a little so that you feel some positive benefits as your breathing and general fitness improve.

AS

Stop smoking: Think of three good reasons why you could stop smoking. Write this down below. Three good reasons I could stop smoking are:

....

....

....

This week

Remind yourself as often as you can of the three good reasons for stopping smoking that you have written above. Use these to help you reduce the number of cigarettes you smoke each day by as many as you can.

Alcohol

Drinking excessively will not help you to feel calm.

Moderation. Drinking alcohol carefully and in moderation can be an enjoyable and often sociable way to unwind after a long week.

The advised limits to drinking sensibly are:
For men – 3-4 units a day; no more than 21 units a week.
For women – 2-3 units a day; no more than 14 units a week.

Drinking within these levels is a healthy way to relax and unwind.
Drinking more alcohol than this can increase your stress levels.

'Low Alcohol' Drinks	Bottle (330ml)	Can (440ml)	Pint (568ml)	Litre
Beer, Lager & Cider at 2%	0.7 units	0.9. units	1.1 units	2 units
Beer, Lager & Cider	Bottle (330ml)	Can (440ml)	Pint (568ml)	Litre
4%	1.3 units	1.8 units	2.3 units	4 units
5%	1.7 units	2.2 units	2.8 units	5 units
6%	2 units	2.6 units	3.4 units	6 units
'Super Strength' drinks	Bottle (330ml)	Can (440ml)	Pint (568ml)	Litre
Beer, Lager & Cider at 9%	3 units	4 units	5.1 units	9 units
Alcopops (5%)	1 Bottle (275ml)			
	1.4 units	–	–	–
Spirits (38-40%)	Small measure (25ml)	Large measure (35ml)	Small double measure (50ml)	Large double measure (70ml)
Gin, rum, vodka & whisky	1 unit	1.4 units	1.9 - 2 units	2.7 - 2.8 units
Shots (38-40%)	Small measure (25ml)	Large measure (35ml)		
Tequila, Sambuca	1 unit	1.3 units	–	–
Wine & Champagne (red, white, rose or sparkling)	Small glass (125ml)	Standard glass (175ml)	Large glass (250ml)	Bottle (750ml)
10%	1.25 units	1.75 units	2.5 units	7.5 units
11%	1.4 units	1.9 units	2.8 units	8.3 units
12%	1.5 units	2.1 units	3 units	9 units
13%	1.6 units	2.3 units	3.3 units	9.8 units
14%	1.75 units	2.5 units	3.5 units	10.5 units
Fortified Wine (17.5-20%)	Standard measure (50ml)			
Tequila, Sambuca	0.9 - 1 unit	–	–	–

Source: NHS Choices website: www.units.nhs.uk/howMany.html

How can excessive alcohol consumption cause stress?
- The more you drink, the more you need to drink to get the desired relaxing results.
- Knowing you are drinking too much can make you stressed.
- It can lead to arguments with friends and family and even problems with the Police.
- It can lead to secondary issues such as a poor diet, less activity, increased smoking and drug taking.
- You put on weight and your general health level decreases.
- Sleep patterns are adversely affected.
- Hangovers make it more difficult to concentrate on even the most straightforward task.
- Productivity at work can be affected.
- Alcohol can lead to worsening feelings of anxiety and depression.
- Drinking too much can contribute to stressful financial problems.

How can I reduce my alcohol intake? Try the following practical method:

Monitor and reduce gradually. If you think that you may be drinking too much - monitor your intake of alcohol. How much are you drinking over an average week – could it be doing more harm than good? If so, try cutting down your weekly intake by a small amount initially. If you start off by reducing your intake by a little, and then feel good for doing so, it is more likely that you will be able to stick to it. You may then wish to make further gradual weekly reductions in the future. Remember to watch the size of your glass when drinking wine.

For example, if you are drinking 3 pints of standard lager each night of the week (that's around 42 units/week), you could try and cut that daily amount to 2 pints to start with. This would cut your weekly figure to 28 units – a 33% reduction which you would probably barely miss. Once you have got used to that, you may decide not to drink any alcohol on Monday and Tuesday (you should have at least 2 days a week without alcohol). This would cut your weekly intake to 20 units - which is below the recommended limit for men. If your colleagues drink excessively, limit the time you spend with them in bars or pubs.

For further help or advice about your alcohol use visit your GP or call Drinkline on 0800 917 8282.

Hugh says:
I like an occasional glass of wine when I get home from work. During the week I normally limit myself to no more than 2 glasses. I drink slowly and enjoy the taste as much as the feeling. I drink water too to keep hydrated. I make sure that I have at least 2 evenings when I don't have any alcohol, but allow myself more than 2 glasses at the weekend if I feel like it!

Work out your alcohol intake over the last week: Tally up the units as accurately as you can.

The number of alcohol units I drank last week was:

....

This week

If your figure for the number of units you drank last week is less or equal to the recommended limits (14 for women; 21 for men) – maintain that this week. If your figure is over this amount, try cutting down by a small amount.

Getting started on Step 6...

...Today, tomorrow and this week: Plan for this step by working out a menu for the week and then carrying out a weekly shop. Reduce items from 'the red list' and increase items from 'the green list' on your shopping list. This will help you to enjoy home cooking, eat regularly and eat healthily. You will start to feel the many benefits of eating in this way (and save some money too).

Don't forget – you don't need to miss out on all your favourite treats, just keep to the 80:20 principle. At every mealtime eat as mindfully as possible – enjoy every mouthful – and stop when you are full. If you don't usually, try to keep within the recommended limit for alcohol consumption. Does this help you feel more alert, get more done and leave your wallet a little heavier?

If you smoke, use today as a fresh attempt to stop or cut back – why not book an appointment today to see your GP to discuss giving up? You'll never regret it...

Jack

Jack

Things have started to change. I am determined to become fitter, healthier and lose 1 stone over the next six months (about 2lbs a month). I now eat regularly every day - making time for a light lunch with mid-morning and afternoon snacks to keep me going. My take-outs at night have been replaced by a house rota for home cooking three nights a week. I now feel much more in control of my diet. On Saturday, I do a weekly shop and, with the help of my housemates, I am trying to get to grips with buying more 'green list' healthy foods and avoid more of the unhealthier 'red list' foods. I'm now more interested in the types of food I eat. This is not hard, it's just knowing what's what.

I have to be strong and remind myself what I am doing, and why, but I feel that I am beginning to develop healthier eating habits. In following the 80:20 rule I still treat myself at the weekend with a pizza, crisps and ice-cream!

I have started to noticed that I am feeling more energetic and am managing to get more done at home and at work.

I'm still an occasional smoker but I'm using the 'Active Steps' project to spur me on to stop. I've been cutting down over the last few weeks and am determined to quit completely. Alcohol intake is also coming down – I've started seeing the bar as my place of work rather than my home-from-home. When I've finished my shift, and unless it's the weekend, I head straight home or to the gym. Monday to Thursday are now non-alcohol nights completely.

As you can see, I've made some practical changes to my lifestyle. Now that I have started to exercise more, eat healthily and smoke and drink less – I can tell you that I feel much better. Getting up in the morning is easier and I have bags more energy throughout the day. People have even started to compliment me on my appearance! This feels good and has given me the confidence and motivation to persist with these changes.

Step 7 Create a calm home

As we often spend much of our week at home, having a relaxing home environment is very important.

Home should be a place where we can relax fully. Here are a few ideas to help you do so.

In this step we discuss how you can:
- ✓ De-clutter your home.
- ✓ Keep a clean home.
- ✓ Enjoy some greenery.
- ✓ Apply the finishing touches: music, scents and lighting.

De-clutter your home

Think of an uncluttered house as a stress-free mind.

It is easy to let possessions build up over time to a stage where you not only have far more than you need, but your home can feel darker and colder.

Despite what people may say, it is more difficult to find things in a cluttered home.

How can I de-clutter?
- ✓ Regularly give away or throw away unused clothes and books.
- ✓ File away paperwork and bills as soon as they have been dealt with.
- ✓ Shred any paperwork you do not need to keep but which has sensitive information on it (small shredders are not expensive).
- ✓ Store things in cupboards and cabinets wherever possible.
- ✓ Don't cover windows or doorways with furniture.

Feng Shui. If you would like to learn more about de-cluttering your home, look into some of the ideas from the ancient art of Feng Shui. Try reading *'Clear Your Clutter'* by Karen Kingston.

Home and work. In the meantime, keep every room as clutter free as possible. Regularly clear out unused and unwanted possessions. This can apply equally to your office space so make sure you regularly de-clutter your place of work too.

Bottlebank   **Shred**   **Recycle**

**Clothes & old paperbacks -
take to a charity shop**

James says:
I used to find it difficult to throw or give away anything. Now I have a weekly, and bigger monthly, de-clutter which re-energises me and my home.

De-clutter your home: **Decide on one room in your home which could most benefit from being de-cluttered. Write this down below.**

One room in my home which could most benefit from being de-cluttered is:

....

This week

Schedule 30 minutes this week to de-clutter this room. Write down when you will do this on your calendar or diary. Be tidy, and if necessary, be ruthless! If this feels good, plan to de-clutter another room too.

Keep a clean home

Stay on top of household cleaning each week.

"This house is dirty. I need to clean it!" **Letting household chores build up can not only leave you living in a dirty home, but also with a constant voice nagging you in the back of your mind.**

How can I keep on top of the cleaning?
- ✓ Doing the washing up straight away after eating.
- ✓ Setting a regular time each week to vacuum and dust, therefore making it more of a routine.
- ✓ Cleaning the house with your family or housemates; make it a time when you can all do it together.

✓   Having your favourite music on while you clean.
✓   Schedule a favourite pastime for when you finish.

Stay in control of your chores with a regular cleaning routine.

James says:
Like putting on clean clothes or getting into a bed with freshly washed sheets, walking into a clean home feels good.

Clean your home: Decide on a set period each and every week to spend 30 minutes cleaning in your home. Write this below and on your calendar.

I will carry out a 30 minute clean each week on a:

....

This week

Carry out your 30 minute clean, as planned. Get yourself some cleaning cloths, window and glass cleaner, wood polish spray and scented multi-surface cleaner. Put some of your favourite music on while you do it and do something fun afterwards.

Enjoy some greenery

Make your home feel a calmer place with some greenery.

Alive. This will also make a change from electrical items and cold, lifeless objects. Plants are alive and can help you feel so too, just a little bit more.

What plants can I keep?
- ✓ A potted plant in your living room.
- ✓ Some herbs in your kitchen or on a window shelf.
- ✓ Some cacti (very low maintenance!).

Hugh says:
I have various types of greenery and fresh flowers around the house and in my office. They brighten up both places.

Buy some greenery for your home: Do you know where your nearest garden centre is? If not, have a look in the yellow pages or online. Write down the name of the garden centre and the address below.

The nearest garden centre to me is:

....

Address:

....

....

Visit the garden centre and have a look for some appropriate and manageable greenery for your home. If you are unsure, ask for some help from someone who works there.

Apply the finishing touches: music, scents and lighting

Relaxing smells, sights and sounds can help you feel calmer at home.

How can I apply the finishing touches to my home?
*   Calming music to have on instead of the TV. If you have digital radio or TV try Chill FM or Classical FM. Otherwise, try any music that helps you to relax.
*   Calming joss-sticks or aromatherapy oils to put on when you get in after work. Lots of specialist shops, supermarkets and even newsagents may stock these. You could also buy online. Joss-sticks may be cheaper, but if used sparingly aromatherapy oils may last you longer and end up being more cost-effective. Have a look at your options.
*   Dim lighting such as low-watt bulbs or candles. Your local supermarket should stock both of these.

Sometime in the next week try an experiment to create as calming an atmosphere as you can at home:

1) Set-up: Switch the TV off, mood lighting and music on and light some calming scents.

2) Relax: Have a warm milky drink or a small glass of wine and open a good book.

3) How does that make you feel?

> James says:
> Search out an album by Virginia Astley called '*From Gardens Where We Feel Secure*.' It's the sound of an English country garden in the summertime – the perfect Sunday morning soundtrack. Amazon's your best bet.

Apply calming finishing touches to your home: Write down which calming music (radio station or CD), scents and lighting you would like to use at home this week to help relax you.

Calming music I would like to try:

....

Calming scents I would like to try:

....

Calming lighting I would like to try:

....

This week

Gather the music, scents and lighting that you would like to try and pick an evening to try them all out together.

Getting started on Step 7...

...Today, tomorrow and this week: You can split this step up into 3 parts: 1) clean/de-clutter; 2) visit the garden centre; and 3) apply the finishing touches. So, start from number 1 and aim to achieve number 3 by the end of the week. It will be a real treat to sit down at the end of the week in your clean, uncluttered, green and calming home with a cup of tea or glass of wine.

Jack

My flat used to be just like my diet – full of junk. Living with three other people didn't help. But there was nothing worse after a long shift than coming home, tripping over stuff in the hallway and walking into a kitchen still full of dirty pots and pans from yesterday's meal – whoever's mess it is. My flat should've been my sanctuary, but it was more of a pigsty. I couldn't live like this any longer, so I decided to take the 'pig by the horns' and sort it!

First things first: I enlisted the help of my reluctant flatmates and ruthlessly threw out all the stuff that we no longer had a use for. We'd had some of it for years. Most of it had been used/read/eaten once, and then left in the bottom of some drawer or cupboard to gather dust. After that, we gave everything a good clean and polish. I sorted out my room too. I organised my magazines, CDs and other odds and ends into shelves or boxes, keeping the floor space clearer. I found quite a lot of old stuff which I didn't realise I still had and out it went. We keep on top of things now with the weekly 'team clean', as we call it. It can actually be quite fun – whack something funky on the stereo, and we're off!

It feels like we have a lot more pride in our place now. We added a potted plant to the lounge the other day. I love the flat being like this. Looking back, I think our messy flat used to make me feel quite uncomfortable. Now that it's clean and tidy I feel so much more relaxed when I'm at home. Coming home is a real luxury and I love spending time there.

Step 8 Balance your lifestyle

Finding a balance on a daily basis between the responsibilities and needs of our work, our family and friends and ourselves is tricky.

It's easy to spend too much of our time and energy on one part of our lives and neglect others.

This can be stressful if we feel we are letting ourselves or others down.

It can also be a problem for us if we are over-indulging in unhealthy lifestyles.

Planning for, and sticking to, a balanced lifestyle can help you feel more in control of your day-to-day life.

You will feel a lot calmer for it.

In this step:
- ✓ Work, rest and play.
- ✓ Get into good sleep patterns.
- ✓ Keep a routine but experiment with change.

Work, rest and play

Keeping a balance can help you feel calm and more in control.

Consumed with work. It can be easy sometimes to become over-involved with our job, especially if we have pressure put on us by our boss, are constantly worried about paying bills, or just find it difficult to 'turn off'.

Time away. It is important, however, to be able to have time away from work, which actually means *not doing, thinking or talking about* work.

Important stuff. During this time you can focus on other important stuff such as friends, loved ones, getting some exercise, your creativity and relaxation.

Helping you feel calm. All of these activities will help you feel calmer, more balanced and in control.

So how can we try to keep a balance?
1) Once you leave work, leave work behind mentally too. You will need to be strict with yourself (and maybe your colleagues and boss) about the amount of time you spend working.

2) Release time by cutting down on less rewarding activities such as watching TV or time in the pub.

3) Plan when you'll have time to do the things you want to do; spend time with family and friends, take some form of exercise, do something creative, relaxing fully with a good book, a hot bath or a relaxation exercise.

4) Do it! Make sure you put your plans into practice.

We will discuss a great selection of relaxation techniques in Step 11.

Hugh says:
The evening is a good time to relax and switch off. After dinner, I finish off any house stuff that needs to be done like bills or letters. I then set aside some time to play guitar or phone a friend to catch up. I like to watch a little TV – I usually catch the news before reading for a while.

Balance out the time you work, rest and play today: **How are you going to balance out your day?**

Work: what will you achieve today in your job/profession, housework or with any fun projects you have on the go?

....

Rest: when and how will you relax today?

....

Play: what exercise will you take, what creative pursuits will you work on and/or who will you meet or call for a catch up?

....

This week

Try to find the time to work, rest and play each day. You will feel good for doing this.

Get into good sleeping patterns

Relax properly before bed and get into regular sleeping patterns.

Feeling tired when you have an important, difficult or long day ahead of you can make things very stressful. We all know the feeling and it's not very nice.

Different people seem to get by on different amounts of sleep. How much sleep do you need?

Irregular patterns of nights out on the town, staying up late watching TV or playing computer games, mixed with assorted early starts and lie-ins are a recipe for a poor sleep pattern and tiredness.

How can I get into a good sleeping pattern?
* Get into a routine of going to sleep and getting up at the same times each evening and morning.
* Take exercise in the day and/or go for a relaxing walk in the evening.
* Have a warm milky drink rather than anything with caffeine or alcohol before bed.
* Write down any thoughts you have or things you need to do tomorrow (at home or at work) so your mind is clear.
* Relax for an hour before bed with a bath or reading a book rather than watching TV.
* Try a relaxation exercise before bed (see Step 11).
* Don't eat a large meal too soon before bed.
* Avoid smoking before bed as this will stimulate your mind.
* Turn off mobile phones and computers.
* Make sure your bed is comfortable and your bedding clean.
* Control the amount of light coming in – is it dark enough?
* Control the temperature so it's just right for you.

Programme yourself. Getting into a routine will allow you to begin to programme yourself for sleep. Before long your body clock should prepare you for sleep and wake you automatically when it's time to get up.

If you have problems sleeping, don't just lie there tossing and turning, try reading until you feel your eyes getting heavy. If you still can't sleep – get up and do some housework till you feel sleepy. Whatever happens, try not to let yourself get worked up. It's not the end of the world if you miss out on a few hours, no matter how important your day is 'tomorrow'.

Try keeping a sleep diary where you write down what you do before going to bed, how often you wake up, and how you managed to go back to sleep. This can help you become more aware of what works for you and what doesn't.

James says:
I like a repetitive background sound, so often sleep with a fan on. Of course, it keeps the room cool in summer but it also stops me waking up due to neighbours, drunken passers-by or extreme Bristol weather.

AS

Get into a good sleeping pattern starting from tonight: Write down below what time you would like/need to wake up tomorrow morning and then work your way back from there.

The time I need to wake up tomorrow morning:

....

The time I will go to bed tonight to get enough sleep:

....

The time I will start relaxing before bed:

....

This week

Get into a regular sleeping pattern. Go to bed at the same time each evening and set your alarm to wake up at the same time each morning. Make sure you relax before bed and get enough sleep. Does this regular routine help you sleep better and feel more alert in the day?

Keep a routine but experiment with change

Routine can help us remember to do the things we need and want to do.

Framework. Feeling calm while leading a busy, productive and fulfilling life can be tricky without some sort of routine. Routine can give us a regular framework, which if we stick to, can help us get all the things done we need to in any given day or week in order to feel calm. This can really help.

Use your timetable. If you have a work timetable, you already have a starting 'framework' in place. Build your routine around this, adding in fulfilling activities in the gaps.

Write down your plans. Use a notebook, calendar or diary to keep track of your plans to help you remember.

Why not try:
- Regular sleeping patterns.
- A walk or jog first thing in the morning.
- Carrying out the weekly shop each Monday night.
- Having a 'movie evening' with friends each Wednesday.
- Fitting in a gym session every Tuesday and Thursday lunchtime.
- Spend some time on a creative activity every Friday night.
- Carry out a weekly review, plan and prepare for the week ahead each Sunday afternoon.

This is just to show you what you *could* do. The days and the activities can be adapted to you and your schedule.

Don't get stuck in a rut. Although a regular routine can help you get things done and to feel relaxed, carrying out *the same routine* for too long week-in, week-out can leave you feeling bored and in a rut.

Change your routine every once in a while to avoid this happening, still ensuring that you get everything you need done.

New and unplanned activities can be enjoyed to make the most of your days off (such as walks, bike rides or day-trips).

Just head off somewhere different for the day. It doesn't need to cost any money – you can travel on foot.

James says:

I have come to realise that I rely on a good routine in the week to get things done and feel positive, healthy and calm. I find that the biggest threat to my sticking to this routine is lack of sleep and too much to drink on the weekend. My weekends are still fun, but I am now more careful not to let this fun throw me out of kilter for the following week.

Get into a regular routine, but also experiment with change: **Think of one new routine you would like to start this week and one new place you would like to visit on a day off.**

One new routine I will start this week:

....

One new activity I will try, or place I will visit on a day off this week:

....

This week

Organise and start your new routine. Try the new activity or visit the new place that you have written above on your day off as well.

Getting started on Step 8...

...Today, tomorrow and this week: Aim to make each day as 'balanced' as possible. Start with your sleeping and make sure you get to bed at a decent hour each night and then up in the morning in plenty of time to start your day. Can you stick to these bedtimes for the whole week to see how it helps your sleep? Plan to have a healthy balance between your work and your active, social and personal commitments – try not to neglect anything. Can you make this routine work for you regularly? Try something new this week – whether it be a different route to work, a new coffee shop for a break, a new activity in the evening or a fun day out at the weekend.

Jack

I used to live a certain type of balanced lifestyle – I'd either be working on one side of the bar, or drinking on the other! I soon became very bad at finding the time to keep in touch with family and friends. I also wasn't looking after myself. I hardly ever relaxed properly and used to get by on next to no sleep. It's no wonder I started feeling so stressed out. I can see now that I was missing out lots of important stuff.

I now feel that, week-in, week-out, I'm living a much better balanced lifestyle. Less time at the pub has freed up time to do the things that really help me to feel calm and more in control of my life. That said, I always catch up with a group of friends on a Friday night to go to a gig and have a few beers.

I like to keep a healthy routine where possible. Although my working hours vary, I know I can get regular exercise by walking to and from work each day. Every Tuesday night is my photography class. I try to remember to call one member of my family or a friend each morning or evening, depending on work. As I normally get Sundays off, I try to go for a drive into the country – somewhere I haven't been before, somewhere different. My sleeping has really improved. Drinking less alcohol, being more active and allocating a regular 8 hours has all helped.

With the aid of positive routines I can get more things done and feel calmer too.

Lifestyle Summary Illustration

Jack is working on a lifestyle to reduce stress. After a busy week working at the bar, he has a day off and plans to make the most of it.

1) He wakes up

As usual Jack gets up at 8.30am feeling awake and rested. He finds his **good sleeping routine** helps. Jack is going to make the most of his day.

2) Clean the flat

With his favourite music on, Jack sets about **de-cluttering his home** - tidying or throwing away unwanted stuff. He then gives his flat a good **clean**.

3) Workout before lunch

Jack enjoys the **regular exercise** of a swim at his local gym. To keep him going he **visualises the benefits of being active:** how good he will feel after his swim and going on his summer holidays, looking and feeling good.

4) Lunchtime

Jack is **increasing intake from 'the green list'** and has a healthy grilled chicken and avocado sandwich. He is also trying to **reduce items from 'the red list'**, so instead of the usual chocolate dessert afterwards, he has a yoghurt and a piece of fruit. **He eats slowly, enjoying the different flavours and textures.**

5) Change

After lunch Jack decides to **experiment with change** and takes a bus into the countryside. He gets off in a little village and goes for a walk around the old shops as part of his new **active lifestyle.** Feeling creative, he decides to take some interesting photographs too.

6) Back home

Arrives back to a clean home. Jack puts on some **relaxing music, scents and dims the lighting.** Smiling, he orders a take-away - he's eaten well all week, so applying the **80:20 principle**, he thinks he deserves it!

Summary Lifestyle to reduce stress

This section has shown you how small changes to your lifestyle can help you feel a lot calmer. As you did with the 'thinking' section, take a week now to put these lifestyle techniques into practice. Have a go at each **AS** and then continue making progress on each topic by following what we suggest you do **this week**.

Don't expect things to necessarily 'click' straight away. You'll need to keep working at each topic to enjoy the benefits. At the end of the book we will suggest an effective approach to mastering the different sections in this book.

Overleaf is a reminder of the steps and topics in this, the lifestyle section.

Eat and drink healthily

Eat regularly, don't miss meals.
Enjoy more home cooking.
Reduce your intake from 'the red list'.
Eat and drink from 'the green list'.
Eat mindfully – enjoy each and every mouthful.
Apply the 80:20 principle to your eating.
Consider stopping smoking.
Monitor your alcohol consumption.

Get active

Visualise yourself enjoying the benefits of getting active.
Have an active lifestyle: walk or cycle wherever possible.
Carry out regular focussed exercise.
Take relaxation exercise.
Set yourself achievable goals and enjoy it.
Be creative.

Create a calm home

Keep your home clean.
De-clutter your home.
Liven up your home with some greenery.
Use calming music, scents and lighting.

Balance your lifestyle

Balance out the time you work, rest and play.
Get into good sleeping patterns.
Keep a routine but experiment with change.

Work on these steps and topics for the next week. When you return, it will be time to learn about *Communication to reduce stress*.

Section 4 Communication to reduce stress

Wherever we are and whatever we do, we have some contact with other people. This contact can make us feel good and worthwhile or, alternatively, can make us feel alone and insignificant if the conversations are difficult.

Many people do not think they can 'control' their communication. As a result, they can often feel frustrated with the types of relationships and style of communication they have.

If communication is approached in a positive way, however, it can be a big help in reducing the stress of day-to-day life. It can also enhance our sense of well-being and belonging. Even complete strangers can be our allies in the pursuit of increased calmness.

In this section we will look into:
- ✓ Communicating clearly with family, friends, colleagues and acquaintances.
- ✓ Connecting to others with positivity and warmth.

There are many useful Active Steps (**AS**) in this section – some you will already recognise and use, others that are new and can be experimented with.

Get used to observing your actions when you are with people. You can also learn a lot from watching other people around you. They will show you good and bad ways of communicating.

Watch how you talk to others and see how you can incorporate these **AS** to help you feel calmer and more socially confident.

Emma

Hi, my name is Emma. I'm 29 and a single mum. I live in a small flat with Tilly, my 3-year-old daughter. Since Tilly's arrival I have hidden myself away from the world – I have also become more negative and anxious. I'm not sure which came first, really, but I know that they fed each other.

I suppose I had always been a bit shy and perhaps not as confident as I'd like to have been. Over the years I have often found it difficult to express myself in social situations, so have looked to avoid them. I know that once I get going I'm fine, but I sometimes find myself wondering what to say and feeling uncomfortable that what I'd like to say is not of any importance. So, I end up saying very little.

Because I don't show much interest, I reckon that other people think I don't like them – which isn't usually true. The worst is when a friend is having a hard time about something. I want to pick up the phone or go and see them to see if they are OK but often decide not to. Why can't I be more supportive? I also have the tendency to 'blow up' at people out of the blue and for no particular reason. I think that's because I get so frustrated with things. Either way, I end up feeling terrible and quite often leave issues unresolved and playing on my mind.

I have a small group of really good friends. I don't have a lot of time, but try to meet up sometimes in town. I'm never great on the phone – my friends usually phone me, rather than the other way around. I always find it difficult to know when to call and I have Tilly to look after 24/7 too. Or maybe that's just an excuse. I can often go for weeks without speaking to friends, which doesn't seem right somehow.

I know that I feel good when I have a proper chat with someone and would like to do it more regularly with more of my friends. Everyone needs to express how they really feel, don't they?

I want to learn to be a better communicator. I want to offer my friends my support when they need it and also to discuss my real worries and concerns with them. I want to make some new friends too! I hope that having more positive contact with people will make me feel more confident and less anxious. We'll see.

Step 9 Communicate clearly

You are the most important person in this project.

Good friends are valuable too, and your relationship with them can help you feel calmer and happier both at home and at work.

We can all help spread calmness through effective and clear communication skills, and also offer and receive love and support.

Communication skills have been looked at by many researchers and psychologists. It will come as no surprise to you if we tell you that a good conversation has a number of building blocks which, when put together, make relationships easier to manage.

This includes:
- ✓ Starting the conversation.
- ✓ Keeping it going.
- ✓ Sharing interests.
- ✓ Helping some conversation go further.
- ✓ Talking enough but not too much.

When these skills are used confidently and often, you will notice your relationships are more rewarding and will help you feel relaxed and calm.

Make initial connections

Eye contact and smiling is usually appropriate and healthy.

Normal. It is normal to feel stressed on occasions because you find it difficult talking to people. Sometimes, when we are out and about, it can feel like we don't connect with others.

Important. It is important, however, to feel able to, and to actually connect with people in your day. As important as getting 'the job done' at work. As important as getting the weekly shop in. As important as getting some exercise.

Sociable. See yourself as a sociable and friendly person who can regularly initiate small contacts with people you meet, whether you know them or not. These contacts can make you feel good.

Practise. As with most things, practice will help.

This involves:
- ✓ Looking at people.
- ✓ Smiling appropriately.
- ✓ Saying something briefly like, 'Hello', 'How are you', or 'It's a nice day, isn't it?'.

Most people will acknowledge you and return the compliment **by making the same comment or even just smiling back.**

This will make you feel more relaxed and confident. Think about when you could start this ball rolling.

Here are some examples:
- ✓ Leaving your flat or house and walking down the road.
- ✓ At your newsagents.
- ✓ Walking into school or the office.
- ✓ Getting on a bus or train.
- ✓ With someone working at a coffee shop, restaurant or bar.
- ✓ Smile when you make a telephone call.

Try making initial connections the next chance you have. How do people react?

James says:
Sometimes, if I'm feeling down I go for a short walk. I try to make small, positive connections with people, where appropriate. Usually this is just a smile or a brief hello, but if they smile and say hello back it often makes me feel a bit better.

Make initial connections today: Some time in the next hour, put this book down and go for a short walk. Say hello and smile to people where appropriate.

This week

Make more initial connections with people each day. Wherever you are, try to smile and say hello to people. How do they respond? Do they smile back? How does this make *you* feel?

Keep the conversation going

Do you know anyone who is a good communicator?

The next stage. Once you are feeling OK about starting a conversation with someone, the next stage is to keep that conversation going.

If you watch other people talking, you will see them using the following skills:
- ✓ Keeping eye contact most of the time.
- ✓ Smiling.
- ✓ Turning their body towards the other person.
- ✓ Speaking almost at the same speed and volume.
- ✓ Listening a lot – nodding their head; using prompts like 'Uh-huh' or 'Yes, I see'.
- ✓ Asking short questions to keep the other person talking such as 'Tell me more?'; 'What do you mean?'; 'What happened next?'.

When could you use them? Try these situations:
- ✓ You could start with a **friend** whom you know well.
- ✓ Or a **colleague**, who is easy to talk to.
- ✓ Alternatively, a **new acquaintance** as you are getting to know them.
- ✓ Even a **stranger** you stand next to in a queue.

The trick is to try out new skills in a situation *you* find comfortable. Practice will help build up your confidence.

Hugh says:
When I talk to people I sometimes feel shy and sometimes feel confident. However I feel, I find that trying to keep the conversation going using simple verbal or non-verbal cues is helpful. I use this anywhere: in a bus queue, over dinner or as a meeting starts.

Keep conversations going: Arrange to meet a friend some time today for a catch up. Try these basic communication skills to keep a conversation going.

This week

Practise keeping conversations going with friends and acquaintants. As you do this more and more, watch how your confidence increases when you are connecting with people. Your conversations should last longer and help you feel calmer.

Share an interest

Make conversation easy.

You can help any conversation develop by sharing mutual interests.

Try and identify an area of common interest and discuss it a little. If the conversation continues, aim to find two or three other mutual interests.

So, what could this include?:
- A good one to get you started is the weather.
- This may sound like a cliché, but it is something that interests and affects all of us one way or another.
- We often feel good when it's sunny, and a bit down when it's grey.
- We get our fair share of wind, rain, snow and other extremes in the UK too – they can make the most simple journey more challenging.
- They also make a great conversational *ice-breaker*!

What could you talk about, apart from the weather?:
- ✓ A local or national news story – be careful with politics.
- ✓ A sporting team, result or event – past, present or future.
- ✓ Food or drink – everyone enjoys eating and drinking.
- ✓ Families – mothers, fathers, sons, daughters, sisters… etc.
- ✓ Travelling – locally or abroad.
- ✓ Animals – pets or the natural world.
- ✓ Work.

Sharing an interest will help both of you feel that you know each other a little bit better and give you a good starting point for the next time you meet. It can make conversations easier and more enjoyable for you both.

James says:
No matter how different you think you are from someone, you will always have something in common with them.

Share an interest: Write down below the name of three friends or acquaintances you have, as well as one thing in which you share an interest.

Friend/acquaintance 1:

....

We share an interest in:

....

Friend/acquaintance 2:

....

We share an interest in:

....

Friend/acquaintance 3:

....

We share an interest in:

....

This week

Practise thinking what you share in common with people rather than how different you are. Try talking to people about interests that you think you share.

Help the conversation deepen

Get to know them better.

Some conversations don't 'deepen', they are just fun and worthwhile as they are and make you feel good.

But, once you've spoken to someone for a while, you may want to get to know them better. Where can the conversation go from here?

Try helping a discussion along like this:
- ✓ Reflect a feeling – When the other person shows or implies a feeling, just say something short which labels or reflects back that feeling. For example: 'that must have made you angry' or, 'that sounds really difficult' or 'you sound upset over that'.
- ✓ Reflect a meaning – When the other person talks about something complex, help the conversation by reflecting back what you think

> they mean. For example, 'it's frustrating when people don't call back, you don't know what to think' or, 'at least you tried to help; its difficult to know what to do'.
> ✓ Clarify - Clarify what has happened with the other person's story: 'so what happened next?' or, 'did they get back to you?' or, 'sounds like they had a lot on their mind'.

Conversations deepen when one person not only listens, but uses their own words and comments to help the discussion along.

Hugh says:
When I'm listening to people, I try to pick up what they are feeling: fed up, worried or happy. I also try to understand what they are trying to explain to me. I can then say things which show I have listened to them and have an interest in them. It involves being a careful listener.

Help conversations deepen: When you meet one of your friends later - try using small, short comments to help reflect and clarify what your friend has to say. This should help make the conversation be more worthwhile to you both.

This week

Practise reflecting feelings, meanings and clarifying what has happened when you are talking to family, friends or acquaintances.

Make your 50% contribution worthwhile

Have an even conversation.

50:50. Despite what we feel about our social skills, we sometimes talk too little or too much. Most conversations should be 50:50.

Worthwhile. In this topic, we want you to focus on what and how much help your contribution is to making a conversation worthwhile.

Balance. Of course, it doesn't really matter if you're not feeling talkative on occasions, or sometimes get a 'bee in your bonnet', but usually it's good to have balanced chats.

This includes using the following conversational skills to make your conversation helpful:
- ✓ Equal share – Watch how much you talk, try not to go over the 50% line. People 'turn off' if they are 'talked at'.
- ✓ Listen – Listen to what the other person is trying to tell you. Don't get too self-absorbed.
- ✓ Information – Give helpful information which is relevant to the topic.
- ✓ Explanation – Explain, in a pleasant way, your understanding of a difficult point or issue.
- ✓ Feedback – Gently and, at times subtly, give feedback on how the other person acted.
- ✓ Direction – Make a helpful, specific suggestion.
- ✓ Self-disclosure – Tell the other person how something made you feel, or give an example of when something similar occurred in your life.

Use your conversational skills to help the other person feel worthwhile. They will really appreciate it. Don't be over-powering by the amount or strength of what you say.

James says:
Sometimes, if a friend is upset about something, it's good for them to let off steam. But, it's also helpful to them to get some feedback from you, too.

AS

Make your 50% contribution help: **When you meet your friend later, try and make the conversation 50:50.**

This week

Try to make your contribution worthwhile to each conversation you have this week, using the skills mentioned in this topic. Try to make as equal a contribution as possible.

Getting started on Step 9...

...Today, tomorrow and this week: Set out to communicate as clearly as you can with people you already know and those you don't. From the moment you get up in the morning, make the effort to make positive initial connections with people you see. How does this feel? If you stop for a chat – keep the conversation going and share an interest where possible. Aim to help a conversation deepen at least twice today – whether it be on the phone or face-to-face. Make your conversations equal and as worthwhile and helpful as possible.

Emma

Emma

I've been working hard on my communication skills for the last couple of months now. I can remember how shy and anxious I used to be socially. It feels a lot easier talking to people now and I actually feel this has made me more relaxed generally, which has surprised me.

It's amazing how many new people I have met in the last 2 months! Even if some of them have been 10 second 'hellos' down at the shops, it's nice exchanging smiles and greetings with people. It makes me feel that I am more sociable and more alive, I suppose. I've made a real effort to have more eye contact with people and be more confident in making initial connections. It's amazing what can happen – I'm going on my first date in over a year next week with someone I met at the coffee shop....

I've realised that I do share lots in common with people. Once I started to think like that it really helped me open up. I feel better about myself and more confident to find out about people and relate to them. When I pick up Tilly from nursery I stop to have more of a natter now with the other mums. They're a nice bunch and we all share the concerns of having tiny terrors to look after! One of the mums is going to bring her little girl around for tea some time. Tilly is very excited.

Relationships with my friends are moving forward, too. It feels easier – more natural – now to let conversations deepen a little. I feel like I'm getting to know many of them better, and them me. Whoever I talk to, for however long, and whatever about – I try to make the conversation worthwhile and make the other person feel good about themselves.

I still get days when I feel a bit down in the dumps and don't really feel like talking to anyone. But more and more I look forward to going out and bumping into people.

Do you know what the strangest thing is? I've just got to know the name of my neighbour after about 4 years of us living next door to each other. Do you know what the best thing is? I've noticed that Tilly has become more confident and chatty with people too – she's been copying her mum.

Step 10 Exchange positivity and warmth

Our relationships with each other are crucial to our feelings of calmness, well-being, security and belonging.

You can be the clearest communicator in the world but still not get across feelings of positivity and warmth.

In this step we look at how you can:
- ✓ Seek support.
- ✓ Help reassure others.
- ✓ Resolve differences.
- ✓ Spread positivity and warmth.

When you look around at other people - your family, your friends or your colleagues - do they seem sympathetic and warm? Do they come across as positive and energetic? Are they like this all the time or do you notice they have 'good days' and 'bad days'? Do they make you feel good?

Positivity and warmth can be expressed when making new friends, seeing friends again, and also in established relationships. As with all these skills, practice helps.

To use these skills, try to be consistent whether you feel you are having a good day or a bad day. If you feel stressed or unhappy, this is an important time to use these skills. It will start to make you feel a bit better.

Seek support

Talk about it.

Don't isolate yourself. When we have a problem and feel stressed, there is a tendency in all of us to keep this to ourselves. It is not healthy to keep stress in – doing this can make us feel isolated and silly. Stress can feed on itself and, mentally, we make it bigger than it needs to be.

Start to feel better. It is amazing how quickly we can feel better if we bring the problem out in the open by talking to someone about it. Others will show interest and give support. The problem will feel less difficult and distressing.

What do *you* do? Do you tend to tell other people when you feel stressed or under pressure? Or do you tend to bottle things up?

Who could you talk to?
- ✓ Sometimes it is easier to tell someone very close to you.
- ✓ Sometimes it's easier to tell friends or acquaintances.
- ✓ Sometimes it's easier to talk to an expert or someone 'anonymous' on the phone.

Seek support. When you feel stressed, angry or upset, contact someone you feel happy talking to and find an appropriate way to tell them you're not feeling great. They will usually show interest, make helpful suggestions and provide you with support and comfort.

The phrase 'a problem shared is a problem halved' is right, and works.

Hugh says:
I'm lucky because I get to meet a lot of people during the day - colleagues, friends and casual acquaintances. If I'm feeling fed up or stressed, I try to find someone who I can tell. This can be quite light-hearted, not a heart-to-heart. Even just 'labelling' the problem helps.

Seek support: Next time you are stressed, angry or upset, who will you call to seek support?

The person I can call for support when I need it next is

....

This week

Call this person if you find yourself feeling stressed, angry or upset this week. They will probably be pleased that you've asked and happy to help.

Help reassure others

Sharing = caring.

Share company. Anxiety and stress can often be generated or kept going by feeling alone, abnormal or silly. Our contact with others is an ideal chance to help reduce or eliminate each of these three distressing feelings in others. This, by implication, will help to reduce our own feelings of being alone, abnormal or silly.

Shared experience. We all share experience and ideas which can help one another. We all face a variety of issues and challenges in life, whatever age we are, whatever our circumstances are and whether we are at home or at work. Most, if not all, of these situations have been experienced by other people.

Share ideas. Show interest in other people's issues and, where you can, reduce their uncertainty. Monitor your conversations for areas of concern in others. Find out the things the other person has found difficult or makes them stressed. You now know a lot about how to manage stress – share these ideas with other people especially when they are feeling stressed or upset. Try to give them information, rather than advice, about stress reduction and let them use this in their own way.

For example, try to:
- ✓ Listen and understand how they are feeling.
- ✓ Explain the benefits of stress control.
- ✓ Discuss ways in which your thinking, lifestyle, communication and behaviour can help you feel calmer.
- ✓ Talk about what has worked for you.

See yourself occasionally as an expert who can share your life experiences (both successes and failures) with others. They will nearly always be reassured by what you say.

James says:
I try to make use of gaps in my day to call friends and family to see how they are. I do this in the car (hands free), during my lunch break or while on short walks.

Help reassure others: **Has one of your family and friends been feeling down or upset recently? Is there someone who could use your support?**

Someone who could use my support at the moment is:

....

This week

Reach out to a family member or friend whom you think needs some support at the moment. Make the effort to call or visit them, and be prepared to listen to them.

Resolve differences

Conflicts are bound to occur occasionally.

A good way to approach these 'disagreements' is to accept that people will annoy you from time to time and you will also annoy others:
- A friend may not see eye to eye with you.
- A boss may misinterpret your actions.
- A colleague may expect too much.
- A partner or relative may wind you up.

The key is to resolve these (often trivial) issues as soon as possible.

Try the following techniques when attempting to resolve a conflict:
- ✓ Take the first step – be willing to make the first move to discuss and resolve a difficulty.
- ✓ Be warm and compassionate – project positive feelings by paying them a compliment; ensure it is sincere and reasonable.
- ✓ Stay calm – remain in control of your emotions in spite of any provocation. You will be less likely to say something you may regret, and will feel better for it afterwards.
- ✓ Be understanding – of their opinion. Accept that you may actually not have fully understood their opinion and may have been more in the wrong than you originally thought. These may be purely differences of opinions, or may be based on differences of belief (religion, culture, lifestyle).

✓ Compromise – give and take and be prepared to meet in the middle to resolve the issue without giving up your own assertive rights.

✓ Invite constructive feedback – by asking them what you have done wrong or could have done differently. If you do this in a calm, gentle manner you should find you receive more constructive feedback and a more positive resolution to whatever happened.

✓ Say sorry – taking responsibility for your own behaviour will enable you to keep your self-respect intact. Often all people want when you make a mistake is that you say, 'I'm sorry'. Write pleasant, constructive letters or emails, not long, rambling, angry ones. Even if it is only partly your fault, it's good to say sorry.

Don't think about conflicts too personally. Try and sort things out as soon as possible so as not to let the situation or stress levels get out of hand.

James says:
Try to give and take. If you accept that you may have done something to upset someone, they are more likely to accept that the fault is partially theirs too.

Resolve differences: Is there anyone whom you have fallen out with or, perhaps, just not spoken to for a while? Would doing so make you feel good?

Someone I would like to resolve my differences/get back in touch with is:

....

This week

Take the first step today with this person. Follow the approach in this topic. How do you feel afterwards?

Spread positivity and warmth

Inject a sense of positivity into all your conversations and relationships.

We all know that we can sometimes help to light up a room by our approach and the things we say or do. How do we do this?

We do it by:
- ✓ Projecting positive, non-verbal behaviour – such as a smile, the sound of our voice, energetic behaviour, shoulders back and standing straight approach, to look as if we feel OK and have energy to give out.
- ✓ Making positive, general comments about any aspect of the situation – like the weather, or the place where the conversation is happening.
- ✓ Making positive comments about the other person – it's a pleasure to see them, their appearance, their time-keeping, their actions, their work.
- ✓ Making positive comments about something said by the other person.
- ✓ Being as genuine as we can and true to ourselves when we talk to others – try and say what you think…. carefully.
- ✓ Avoiding being judgemental as we are all different and approach life differently – respect that in others and understand where they are coming from.
- ✓ Making positive comments when leaving which makes the other person feel valued, in general, and in particular about this conversation or visit.
- ✓ Feel able to touch the person appropriately – shake their hand, give them a hug, touch their arm.

A pebble in the pond. You know what a pond looks like when a pebble is dropped into it? The ripples caused by the pebble gradually go from one side to the other and then back again. Other pebbles could be producing the same effect in different parts of the pond, and so on... The good feelings generated by being pleasant, warm and positive to others are just like this. If you are warm and compassionate to one person, this produces a positive ripple effect, which makes your local world go round.

Social sunshine. To be positive and warm with family and friends, you need regular contact. Absence does not always make the heart grow fonder. Relationships are not like mushrooms needing to be kept in the dark. They are like seeds or bulbs – they need feeding with social sunshine and water.

Try and spread positivity and warmth with your communication skills every day whether by:
- ✓ Phone.
- ✓ Email.
- ✓ Face to face.

Keep daily contact with, and talk to, family, friends and colleagues. It can really enhance your well-being as you will usually have positive interactions, which will make you feel good.

Do this even (and especially) if you are feeling down, and don't really feel like it.

Hugh says:
I enjoy keeping up with friends and colleagues by phone. Whatever my mood, I tend to talk in a positive and happy way and show interest in their day. I believe that it helps to be warm and kind even in little ways when I speak to them. They nearly always respond the same way, which makes me feel it has been worthwhile.

Spread positivity and warmth: Put the book down now for 5 minutes and use your positive communication skills to call at least one family member or a friend to say hello and see how they are.

This week

Try and call at least two people each day to spread positivity and warmth. Even if you leave a message on their answer-phone, the person you are calling will appreciate that you have taken the effort to call, and that the message you have left is warm and sincere.

Getting started on Step 10...

...Today, tomorrow and this week: Practise being as positive as possible in all conversations you have. How do others react to your positivity? If you sense uncertainty in someone you are speaking to, gently help to increase their self-assurance. Is there one issue or problem that is causing you concern at the moment? Reach out to at least one friend, relative or acquaintance to talk it through. Do you have an unresolved difference with somebody? Or maybe just someone you haven't spoken to for some time? Plan when you will make the time to speak to them.

How does spreading positivity and warmth make others react to you? How does this make you feel?

Emma

I can remember how it used to be. I didn't communicate much with others and when I did, I would typically moan about something or other. It probably wasn't even anything worth worrying about but I got into the habit of being negative about myself, my life and others. As if that somehow made things better. It's not surprising that I didn't feel particularly fulfilled in my relationships a lot of the time, or that I was feeling upset and stressed.

As you know, I've been working on improving my communication skills over the past few months and things have been going well. I now feel more confident talking to people, and have been doing so more on an everyday basis with people I see down at the shops, mums at nursery and friends on the phone.

Lately I've been working more on how I've been talking to others. I'm aware that I used to talk quite negatively so have been trying to be as positive as I can be in conversations, both about others and about myself. It's funny – the more positive I am about myself, my day or my life – the more positive I feel. The more positive I am about others – the more positive they feel and are about me. It seems like a win-win situation and it feels good.

I now try to talk to at least one good friend and one family member each evening, usually when Tilly is tucked up in bed. It's fun just to have a chin-wag but I try to listen to their concerns and reassure them if I can. I find that it's getting easier for me to open up now too. I still have disagreements with people but try and sort them out straightaway.

Yesterday, I took myself by surprise and called up an old friend who I hadn't spoken to for ages. We fell out a while back when we were out drinking – something and nothing. I have had this annoying, nagging voice ever since due to the situation being unresolved. Needless to say, it was great to chat to her and great to get rid of that nagging voice, too!

Summary: Communication to reduce stress

In this section we have looked into the importance of positive relationships with others, and ways to cultivate them. We hope you have completed all the **AS** in this section. If not, have another go at the ones you may have missed. Take the next week to continue practising each topic, following what we suggest you do **this week**. These are ideas that may take a bit of practice, but stay with them even if you find them difficult at first. Don't be put off if you feel you are making 'mistakes', just take the positives out of every conversation you have and your input into them.

It is also worth noting that the skills in this section are often a lot easier to apply when you are feeling in a good mood. When you are feeling a little low or unhappy, having conversations of any nature with others can be the last thing you feel like doing. Try not to let this put you off as this is precisely the time to seek out support from others to help pick yourself up.

Communicate clearly

Make initial connections with people.
Keep the conversation going.
Share an interest.
Help the conversation deepen.
Make your 50% contribution worthwhile.

Exchange positivity and warmth

Seek out support from others.
Help reassure others.
Resolve differences.
Spread positivity and warmth.

Take a week to practise these two steps and their topics. When you have done so, it will be time to move on to the final TLCB section in the book – *Behaviour to reduce stress*.

Summary Illustration

Emma is practising communication to reduce stress. She has a 3 year old daughter, Tilly.

1) Buying some milk

Emma gets up early and walks to the local shop to buy some milk with Tilly. She makes an **initial connection** with the lady at the counter, 'Hi, what a beautiful day'. They exchange smiles.

2) Morning meeting

Emma has an informal meeting with someone about a part-time job. His mobile rings and Emma recognises the ringtone. 'So, you're a U2 fan?', she asks, turning towards him, smiling and **keeping the conversation going**. They talk for 5 minutes, **sharing an interest** in music and the ice is broken.

3) Phone a friend

Just before lunch, Emma calls a friend who she knows has been rather 'down in the dumps' recently. 'Why don't we go for a bite after work?' Emma suggests. 'Don't worry - we'll sort it!' she adds, **helping to reassure** her friend.

4) Late afternoon

Emma leaves her flat to meet her friend. She smiles and says hello to people where appropriate as she's walking down the street, making as many **initial connections** as possible. She realises that other people are acting in a more positive manner towards her as a result, and this makes her feel good.

5) In the café

Emma listens carefully to her friend's concerns and tries to **help the conversation deepen**.
'I know how you feel', Emma says, 'sometimes things get on top of me too. I try to go for
a long walk with Tilly which gives me time to think straight,' **sharing ideas that work**.
When they are finishing their coffees, Emma **reaches out** for some advice from her friend
regarding an argument she has had with her sister.

6) Back home

Emma gets home and is feeling good having supported her friend. She decides to take the
first step and call her sister to talk things through and **resolve their differences**. They
both apologise for their part in the argument. Emma is relaxed and feels she has **spread
positivity and warmth** today. She knows she will sleep well tonight.

Section 5 Behaviour to reduce stress

This section looks at how increased relaxation and personal organisation can help you feel calmer.

You may already recognise and use some of the ideas mentioned. If so, great – carry on with them.

We hope there are some new ideas for you to try too.

In this section we will look at:
- ✓ Relaxation methods to use wherever and whenever.
- ✓ Handling your finances.
- ✓ Organising your home and office systems.
- ✓ Managing your time.

There are many Active Steps (**AS**) in this section. Try them out straightaway with an open mind.

Isha

Hi there, my name is Isha. I'm 52 and live with my partner Ian. I have always had a busy schedule working from and maintaining our home. Having lots to do, it often feels like I hardly have time to sit down during the day – I always seem to be on the go. Occasionally I will stop at lunch time for a quick sandwich and mug of tea but even then I am usually on the go as I eat! Ian works very long hours so deserves my support.

Work is mostly fine – it's quite structured so I just get on with it. It just feels like everything else is out of control – I seem to have great difficulty organising myself. For example, there is the house paperwork. Letters come in the post and get left for days in the kitchen, lounge or wherever else they'd been opened and discarded by me or Ian. It seems that there are piles of unsorted paperwork in drawers everywhere. If I have to find a specific letter, I don't know where to start. I also have difficulty remembering our appointments or family birthdays, which always seem to play on my mind. I have a diary but don't always use it. Quite often an event or work deadline will creep up on me, which I am supposed to have done stuff for in advance but haven't managed to. I usually do a rushed job and feel bad that I haven't realised and sorted it out earlier.

Our finances are another constant worry for me. Ian's salary is good but each month our bank statements show we've gone overdrawn again. I don't know how it keeps happening – I'm sure we are being careful and not wasting money.

I feel like I am rushing around the whole time but not actually getting much done and never getting much chance to relax. I feel under a lot of pressure – physically and mentally stressed. It affects my mood and how I sleep. Sometimes I get quite angry with Ian for no apparent reason, which I hate myself for. I know that I am a caring and conscientious wife, I just think I need to get a bit more organised and relax more.

In an ideal world, I would like the chance to take an evening class – something different. I know I'd enjoy flower-arranging but just don't think I could find the time.

Step 11 Relax more

This is one of the most immediate and practical of all the steps.

Everyday we go from one situation to the next with some feeling of physical or muscular tension or relaxation.

This step addresses how to increase how relaxed you feel, most of the time.

We will show you a number of different relaxation techniques you can try.

The topics we cover in this step include:
- ✓ Use your current ability to relax.
- ✓ Use instant relaxation.
- ✓ Use systematic relaxation.
- ✓ Try guided progressive muscular relaxation (PMR).
- ✓ Let go of unproductive anger.

Soon you will be more confident of being able to relax quickly whenever you want.

Use your current ability to relax

During the day you will often relax for short periods without realising it.

When relaxed, people often describe feeling:
- ✓ Physically **light** or physically **heavy.**
- ✓ **Clear-headed.**
- ✓ At **ease**.

However, we often:
- Aren't aware **when** we relax.
- Don't relax **often**.
- Don't relax **deeply**.
- Don't think we can **switch** relaxing on.

So, when might we relax on a day-to-day basis?

This may be:
- ✓ In the **bath.**
- ✓ Having a **warm drink.**
- ✓ Going for a **quiet walk.**
- ✓ **Reading** a book or paper.
- ✓ At your **desk.**
- ✓ Propping up a wall **talking** to a colleague.

James says:
I find going for a walk relaxing, whether in the city or countryside. I often go for a wander, in no particular direction and clear my head.

You can relax already: Think of three situations in which you often feel relaxed. Write these down below.

Three situations in which I feel relaxed:

....

....

....

This week

Put this current ability to relax into practice more often each day. Feel confident that you are good at relaxing.

Use instant relaxation

This method takes 10 seconds or less. It can be used anywhere and in any position.

This is how you do it:
1) Use a trigger word such as 'relax' to make you pause and think about relaxing.
2) Take a deep breath and let it out slowly and then repeat this process.
3) Get physically comfortable, stretch your shoulders, take several more deep breaths and think calming thoughts.
4) Count slowly from 1 to 10.

Use this approach several times a day **at work or at home. As your** confidence builds, you will find it easier to *instantly* relax and the feeling will last longer.

Use this approach if you feel yourself getting stressed, **angry or frustrated.** You will be able to use it in a traffic jam or to stop yourself getting into an argument with someone.

Use this approach to relax deeper **when you are already feeling calm. A** visual reminder (like a photo, or a funny or child-like object) can help you train yourself to do this regularly.

> Hugh says:
> I use the word or image 'relax' in as many places as I can. When I'm driving in traffic, sitting at a 'busy' desk, doing the washing up or standing in a long supermarket check-out queue. I can feel the pleasant, warm feeling going through my body and mind. It can last 10 seconds or 10 minutes.

Use instant relaxation **to relax you. Put the book down and try it now.**

This week

Use instant relaxation regularly each day. Experiment with doing it as often as you can each day. How does it make you feel?

Use systematic relaxation

Appreciate the difference between tensed and relaxed muscles.

It takes about 5 minutes and can be done anywhere.

This is how you do it:
1) Sit or lie down in a quiet and comfortable place.

2) Breathe in through your nose, filling your lungs so your stomach muscles stretch. When you breathe out, let go of the tension in your body. As you breathe out, notice the difference between feeling tense and feeling relaxed. This will help you to practise 'bringing on' the relaxation of tense muscles more often.

3) Tense and relax over the whole of your body. Think about each of the following five main groups, one by one: your face; hands and arms; back, neck, shoulders; stomach; and your legs and feet. Go through each of these briefly and start by tensing the muscles. For example - in your face: tense your eyes closed, your forehead, your lips and teeth and count to 5. Then relax and 'let go'. Breathe slowly to deepen this relaxing feeling.

4) Practise. You can practise this systematic relaxation method every day or twice a day – it doesn't take long. You can even do this in a busy home or office by closing the door and advertising the fact that you want 5 minutes undisturbed time to yourself.

Hugh says:
I do this sitting on a comfortable chair indoors if I have 5 minutes spare. The phrase 'letting go' is a good one for me as I do this. After a few minutes, I'm feeling calmer and ready to move on to what's next.

Practise systematic relaxation: When can you try this 5 minute method today and where you will do it? Write this down below.

When I will try systematic relaxation today:

....

Where I will try it out:

....

This week

Schedule to practise systematic relaxation twice each day. When and where will you do this? How does it make you feel?

Try guided progressive muscular relaxation (PMR)

There are instructions on the CD provided.

To really let go and allow yourself to relax deeply, it can help to listen to someone else's voice and let them guide you through the relaxation process.

On the accompanying CD, you will find a 20-minute exercise where you will be guided through a series of instructions to tense and relax muscles.

There are 4 tracks so if you get interrupted you can return approximately to where you left off.

Listen to this regularly, you will find your skill in relaxing deeply will significantly increase.

This will also help you to relax more deeply when you relax *instantly* or *systematically*.

> James says:
> Listen to this CD if you are feeling a bit tense, but also when you are feeling calm – to help you feel even *calmer*.

Use PMR: When and where can you listen to the CD either today or tomorrow? This will take 20 minutes.

When I can listen to the CD:

....

Where I can listen to the CD:

....

This week

Schedule at least one more occasion when you can listen to this CD this week to feel fully relaxed.

Let go of unproductive anger

There are ways to manage it.

Evolution. Mankind has used anger as a way to react instantly to a perceived risk to ourselves, or others. This can still be applied in the present day.

Constructive. If managed and channelled properly, this anger can be used constructively. It can be a strong and productive motivator for us to work hard.

Unnecessary. But most occasions in which we can feel ourselves getting angry are not matters of *life or death*. Yet we all get angry at times. Sometimes we just need to…. *let go.*

Calmness = control. Stress and anger go together in much the same way as calmness and relaxation. When we are calm and relaxed we feel in control and contented.

Anger = lack of control. When we are stressed and angry, we can often lose control and react instantly without thinking. This may make us feel more powerful in the short-term, especially if we get our way. In the long-term, however, it can lead to a loss of respect from others, a loss of self-respect and a feeling of isolation.

Manage it. Whether you feel that you are getting angry with someone else, yourself, the world or with a computer or a traffic jam – there are ways to manage it.

Try the following anger management plan if you feel yourself getting angry:

1) Stop. Stop yourself from saying or doing anything irrationally in response to this anger.

2) Take control. Tell yourself, "I can cope in this situation without losing my cool".

3) Use instant relaxation to relax you. **Tell yourself to relax, take several deep breaths, physically relax and use some calm imagery. Do this for at least 30 seconds.**

4) Change negative, irrational and unproductive thoughts into positive, rational and productive ones:
>   "I have nothing to gain from getting angry".
>   "I am a calm and positive person".
>   "This feeling will pass".
>   "I am not going to get angry".

5) Make a calm decision. **If you are still feeling angry, choose from one or a combination of the following:**

Walk away. **If you feel that you have nothing to gain from trying to sort things out or that you are too angry to do so.**

Be assertive. **Express how you are feeling in a calm and logical manner. This will help others understand how you are feeling and help you feel more confident about handling your anger.**

Seek support. **Phone a partner, friend, family member or colleague for a chat about how you are feeling. Explain that you are trying not to get angry and they should help you remain calm.**

Forgive and forget. **Let go of the anger and move on from the situation.**

> James says:
> I used to get angry quite regularly, particularly when driving. Now if I'm in the car and someone's winding me up I try to ignore them. If it's on the motorway, I let them pass safely.

Let go of unproductive anger: Think of one or two situations now that have made you angry in the past week and practise the 5-step process.

This week

The next time you feel yourself getting angry, tell yourself to 'stop' and follow the 5-step anger management plan.

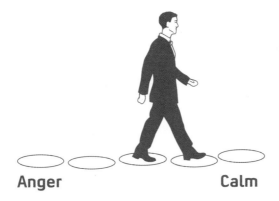

Anger   **Calm**

Getting started on Step 11...

...Today, tomorrow and this week: Practise spontaneous and planned relaxation. Plan when you will have time to try systematic relaxation and PMR – could this be first thing in the morning, at lunch or in the evening? Write down these plans in your notebook, diary and/or calendar to help you remember.

Use your current ability to relax, and try instant relaxation, at regular intervals throughout the day if you start to feel a little stressed or tense, or just to relax deeper.

If you feel yourself getting at all worked up or angry practise the 5-step anger management plan.

Isha

I used to be in a constant state of stress. Every day seemed the same – get up, sort the house out, do some work, do jobs... and eventually stop to go to bed. But I wasn't looking after myself.

For the last couple of months I have been prioritising relaxing more each day. I now have a good routine which really helps me to stay physically and mentally calm. Each morning I get up, and before getting breakfast on the go, I allow myself a couple of minutes of instant relaxation to start the day on the right note. Before lunch, I schedule 10 minutes systematic relaxation. I find that this allows me to calm myself down after a busy morning. I then make sure that I sit down for a quiet lunch before starting the afternoon. Throughout the day I try to practise instant relaxation if I'm feeling a bit tense or stressed – it doesn't take long and it usually does the trick.

I really feel that I am now allowing myself to relax more often and more fully, and that this is having a positive effect on me and my relationship with Ian. I seem to be able to get a lot more done each day; I sleep better and generally feel and act a lot calmer.

Step 12 Handle your finances

We need money for everything from our basic home utilities and food, to our clothes, to our luxury items including holidays and cars.

Although we only need to have the basics, even the basics can cost enough to put us under financial pressure. Combine this with the pressure from advertisements for the 'next big' important gadget or gizmo, Xbox or iPod that we 'can't live without', and this pressure grows still further.

The problem is: if we spend more than we earn, and this is not rectified quickly, we soon end up in debt. Add credit-card use and loans to this and our finances can soon get out of hand.

It may take some small readjustments, but better financial control is possible. Living within your means will help you feel a lot calmer.

The key to handling your finances is recognising the benefits of keeping within your budget.

The topics in this step are:
- ✓ Work out your day-to-day spending.
- ✓ Work out your bills.
- ✓ Work out your income.
- ✓ Work out what you can afford.
- ✓ Save money.
- ✓ Put some money away.

Work out your day-to-day spending

The stress of knowing is better than the stress of not knowing.

Scary truth? Finding out exactly how much money we spend, and what we spend it on, can be something we don't really want to do. Perhaps we feel we have better things to do, or that the prospect of finding out *the truth* about our spending is too scary.

Rectify. Either way – the stress of knowing is better than the stress of not knowing. It gives us the chance to rectify the situation before things get worse.

So what do you need to do?

1) How much? The first thing to do is work out how much you are spending each week. Can you afford to spend this much?

2) On what? And what you are spending this money on? Can you reduce this somehow? At this stage we are not referring to household bills or debts, but everyday expenditure such as food and drink, transport (bus fare, petrol), clothing and luxury items. Anything that you go out and *buy*.

3) Money notebook. To make this a little easier, get yourself a small notebook in which to write down everything you buy. Find out where your hard-earned money *really* goes.

4) Day-to-day. Write down all your regular everyday expenditure such as your morning paper, the coffee on the way to work, the bus fare and your evening food.

5) Luxury. For some of your expenditure, such as clothing, you may need to work out how much you usually spend in a month and divide this figure by four to get your weekly amount.

6) Overestimate. It is advisable to overestimate if in doubt, as we usually spend more than we think rather than less.

7) Weekly amount. Finish with a weekly amount for how much you spend in total.

8) Itemise. You can also work out the amount you spend on individual items – such as food, alcohol, clothes, cigarettes, take-aways, magazines etc. Some of these figures may surprise you.

Approach this inquisitively – 'I wonder how much I really spend and on what'.

Approach this positively – 'Finding out the truth will help me get on top of my finances and feel calmer'.

> James says:
> This can be a really insightful process. When I first did this, I was surprised how much I spent on cigarettes (this was one of the reasons I stopped), alcohol and eating out. It helped me to work out how to spend less, but also how to allocate money to the things I would really appreciate (like music, travelling, books and good food at home).

Monitor your day-to-day spending: Write yourself a reminder now to buy yourself a little black book to help monitor your spending.

This week

Write down all your spending for at least the next 7 days.

Work out your bills

How much of your income do you need to allocate to your bills?

This includes:
- ✓ Mortgages.
- ✓ All household bills.
- ✓ Mobile phone bills.
- ✓ Debt repayments.
- ✓ Car repayments.
- ✓ Insurance.
- ✓ Any other regular bills.

These will usually be either:
- Yearly.
- Quarterly.
- Monthly.

You should be able to work them out through your:
- ✓ Bank records.
- ✓ Cheque book stubs.
- ✓ Invoices/bills.

Be thorough in adding up these amounts into a monthly or yearly figure from which you can work out how much of your income you need to allocate per week or month towards your bills.

Weekly vs. monthly. Do you get paid or pay yourself on a weekly or monthly basis? If paid weekly, work out what your expenditure is on bills per week.

It shouldn't take longer than an hour to calculate, although this is dependent on how many bills you have.

Hugh says:
If I look at the information I get from my bank, I can have a good idea of what I'm spending each month. Sometimes I stop doing this for a month or two and, guess what? My spending goes up and up.

Work out your bills: Go to your bank to get a print-out of all your direct debits and standing orders.

This week

Add up all your yearly bills and divide by 52 or 12 to give you a weekly or monthly figure.

Work out your income

Now, how much do you have coming in?

This includes your:
- ✓ **Salary**.
- ✓ **Interest** on any savings or investments.
- ✓ **Pensions**.
- ✓ State **benefits**.

Once again, work out a weekly or monthly figure.

Ensure you save funds for your tax bill (if employed, you are probably not responsible for saving your own tax).

Work out your income: Write down your income below, or on a separate piece of paper.

My yearly salary before tax:

....

My yearly salary after tax:

....

Interest on savings:

....

This week

Add up your yearly income (after tax) and divide by 52 or 12 to give you a weekly or monthly figure.

Work out what you can afford

What is your disposable income?

weekly or monthly *income*

- (minus)

your figure for weekly or monthly *bills*

= what your weekly or monthly *budget* is for day-to-day expenditure.

An obvious way to increase the amount of money you have available to you, without increasing your income, is to become more efficient and reduce the amount of money you spend.

Do you think you could cut down on your spending somewhere?

Hugh says:
It's essential that I know what I need to spend each month and whether I can afford it. This means I must keep on top of the figures and relevant paperwork. It's not as difficult as it sounds but I need to keep an eye on it all and not ignore it.

Work out what weekly day-to-day expenditure you can afford:
Subtract weekly bills from weekly income.

Weekly bills (a) =

....

Weekly income (b) =

....

Weekly budget (b-a)=

....

This week

Aim to keep within this budget.

Save money

This is a good idea whatever your finances are like.

Clarity. You should now have a much better idea of your own finances.

Necessity or choice. You may feel you have to reduce expenditure (because you are in debt or are spending too much) or would like to reduce expenditure (to have more disposable money for day-to-day spending, a rainy day or a special event).

There are plenty of practical ways for you to start doing this:

1) Reduce household bills
- ✓ Check on **www.buy.co.uk** to see if all your insurance, gas, electricity, telephone, broadband and digital bills are as cheap as you can get them. You could save hundreds of pounds a year by **switching provider**.
- ✓ Don't leave **electrical items** on standby.
- ✓ Turn the **thermostat down** a degree or two.
- ✓ Have an **extra jumper** on rather than the heating.
- ✓ Turn all **lights off** when not in use.
- ✓ Only fill the **kettle** with as much water as needed.
- ✓ Use energy efficient **light bulbs**.
- ✓ Reduce your use of **phones**, especially at peak times **(email is free)**.

2) Reduce food and drink expenditure
- ✓ Supermarkets vary in their prices and you can get your fruit and vegetables cheaper from markets. **Compare prices** of supermarkets at **www.trollydolly.co.uk** or **www.madaboutbargains.com**.
- ✓ **Plan** what meals you will have for a week and what you will need to buy so you shop more efficiently.
- ✓ Reduce the amount of food you waste. **Use up leftovers**.
- ✓ Don't shop on an **empty stomach** – we often buy more than we otherwise would.
- ✓ Take a **packed lunch** to work.
- ✓ Cut down on **take-aways** – they are often expensive *and* unhealthy.
- ✓ Reduce the number of **coffees** you buy – costing around £2 a go this adds up to around £500 a year if you buy one each working day.

✓ Reduce the amount you spend on **alcohol** each weekend – share a bottle of wine as a treat at home instead.

3) Reduce your luxury spend
✓ If you **don't need** something, **don't buy** it.
✓ **Borrow** something rather than buy it if possible.
✓ Shop from **second hand stores** or charity shops – you can pick up some good quality bargains, plus it can be more fun.
✓ Use **outlet stores** or factory stores.
✓ Why not stay well clear of temptation altogether and do something **completely different** and more relaxing instead of shopping?

4) Reduce travel costs
✓ **Walk or cycle** to destinations wherever possible – get some exercise, save money *and* be good to the environment.
✓ Take the **coach** rather than the train – much less expensive.
✓ Shop **locally** if possible.
✓ Buy **online** to reduce cost, travel and time.

5) Carry cash
✓ If you have worked out how much disposable money you have to spend each week after bills, **take cash out** at the start of the week that must last you till the end of the week.
✓ If you do this you can **leave all bank cards at home** and use only cash.
✓ You will **naturally spend less** as 'plastic' somehow never feels like real money.
✓ You will also be able to **see how much money you have** to make last for the rest of the week.
✓ You don't necessarily need to have *all* of the week's money on you *all* of the time. Just **carry enough to get by**.

6) Stop smoking
✓ If you smoke **20 cigarettes a day**, you are probably spending around **£2000 pounds a year** on a product which can make you more stressed through withdrawal, poor health and financial implications.

✓ You can feel a **calmer person** on all these counts once you have stopped smoking.

✓ There is more information on smoking in **Step 6**.

How much money do you think you could save a week, month and year?

James says:
Reducing food waste saves me a lot of money each week. I try to freeze excess food. Leftovers can be put into stews, omelettes or stir fries.

Save money: Write down 3 ways you could save some money, using the above ideas or other ideas of your own.

Three ways I can save money this month:

1) ....

2) ....

3) ....

This week

Put these three ways to save money into regular use.

Put a bit away

Save up for something special or for a rainy day.

New account. Once you feel you are more in control of your weekly and monthly spend, you could consider saving some money in a separate account from your current account.

Margin for error. No matter how careful we are on a day-to-day basis with our finances, unless we have a little money put away one big bill can appear out of nowhere to put us in the red again.

Affordable. Make it a monthly figure you can afford. As little or as much as you can – it will soon add up.

You can set up a savings account for a number of reasons:
- ✓ For **tax** if you are self employed.
- ✓ For a **holiday**.
- ✓ For Christmas time **gifts** and celebrations.
- ✓ For a **rainy day** or unexpected bill.

What are the Active Steps to doing this?

1) Just set up a new account.

2) Work out an affordable weekly or monthly amount to be transferred across.

3) This could be as little as £5 a month.

4) As well as or instead of this, you could have a piggy bank at home to save up your loose change.

How would you feel if you had a bit of money saved away?

Hugh says:
I've always found the concept of saving money difficult. I do now try to save some money each month. I have a savings account where I put something in at the end of each month. I also have a piggy bank at home where I put loose change. This adds up – this year I'm planning on a trip to London to go music shopping.

Set up a new savings account: Go into your local building society and speak to an adviser. See what accounts they have that would be suitable for you.

This week

Set up an account and a monthly standing order to go into it from your bank. Get yourself a piggy bank, keep it at home and start saving up your change.

Further financial advice

If you want further financial advice there are several FREE services available to you.

These include:
The Consumer Credit Counselling Service (Freephone 08001381111).
The National Debtline (Freephone 08088084000).
Your local Citizens Advice Bureau.

Getting started on Step 12...

...Today, tomorrow and this week: Sit down with your bank records and/or bills and work out the difference between your bills and your income to give you a weekly figure that you can afford to spend. You can also work out ways that you can save money at home, with your spending and on travel – why not write some of these down in your notebook and/or stick them on the fridge to help you remember? If you haven't already done so, buy a 'little black book' and carry it around with you this week, noting down how much you spend and on what. Later in the week, set up a savings account with a monthly standing order for whatever you can afford, to be transferred across from your current account or, failing that, start keeping a piggy bank at home.

Isha

Isha

I've always been in charge of the finances, which is fine. The only problem is it's my fault when things go wrong! As a partnership, Ian and I never used to set limits on our spending so we frequently went overdrawn and didn't have enough money for big bills or trips.

I've now got a better handle on what's going on. Over the past month, I've written down our day-to-day spending in a notebook. It's amazing to see how much we spend and on what. We spent £32 on magazines last month (or was that just me?). We spent another £95 on take-aways. Unbelievably, we also spent £150 on cigarettes (that's definitely not me!). It's good to see these figures to really bring home where the money goes and where money could be saved. From my bank records I also worked out what all our various household bills amount to each week. With this done, Ian and I worked out what was coming in after tax and subtracted the 'outs' from it.

Now that we know what we've actually got in the kitty each week, it feels like a weight has been lifted. Although it's less than I'd like, I'm working on ways to make our house run more efficiently in terms of our energy output and what we buy. Ian has agreed to cut-down on cigarettes. If he stops, we've decided to put £100 a month into a savings account for our summer holiday. I've agreed to cut back on some stuff too, so I hope that will be nearer £150.

This week I took out our weekly budget in cash. It definitely felt harder handing it over rather than a plastic card, which is good. I'm confident that we can keep up our financial control over the rest of this year and beyond. I'm already dreaming of drinking a cocktail on the beach this summer. What more incentive could I need?

Step 13 Organise your systems

Do you find it difficult to concentrate calmly on tasks at home or at work due to the constant 'niggle' of disorganisation?

Does your desk seem to have taken on a life of its own as its contents sprawl higher and wider?

We all know how difficult it can be, not to mention uninspiring, to keep on top of an effective system at home and at work for all our correspondence, bills, ongoing jobs, appointments and various projects.

The following approach may take a short time to set up, as well as weekly maintenance, but it will result in you feeling calmer, more in control and motivated to persist with your new systems.

This system can be done at home or at work. For this example we will discuss a home version.

The topics are:
- ✓ Create a filing system.
- ✓ Use a notebook.
- ✓ Keep a calendar.
- ✓ Carry out a weekly review.

Create a filing system

Include everything.

Start. Create a filing system for all your home paperwork.

Individual. Ensure the system includes separate files for everything that is ongoing in your home life at present.

Comprehensive. Include everything from everyday gas bills, to research on the car you would like to buy, to ongoing creative projects.

Here are the Active Steps you can take:
1) Separate paperwork: include bills, instruction booklets, correspondence with particular companies or individuals, research and personal material.
2) Use different envelope files per 'topic'.
3) Label them clearly: this will make the files easier to read and file, and increase your motivation to maintain the system. If you want, you can use printed labels (you can buy label printers from most stationers).
4) File them neatly in a filing cabinet.
5) Review regularly and have a yearly clear out of all bills (into a folder or box file to be stored per company per year) and material you no longer think you need.

James says:
I have separate files for different home utilities and correspondence as well as for the things I'm interested in, such as photography, music and ideas for presents.

Create a filing system: Get yourself around 20 flat office files from a stationers.

This week

Spend some time at home going through your paperwork creating clearly labelled, separate files of different bills, correspondence and interests.

Use a notebook

A more comprehensive and efficient version of your everyday 'to do' list.

Buy a notebook, such as a reporter's pad, from any stationers, so you can rip out old notes that are no longer needed.

Use this notebook regularly to help you relax a little more in the knowledge that all your ongoing jobs and projects are written down somewhere.

This will allow you to concentrate fully and calmly on whatever you are focussing on to do at the present time.

Split the notebook into 2 sections:

1) To do list (at front)
- ✓ This is your **day-to-day list** of what you need to get done.
- ✓ This could include home, work, family, shopping tasks – **any jobs you have** to do.
- ✓ Rather than just write down a list of outcomes, try to think of your daily list in terms of what **Active Steps** you need to do in order to move towards completing the task. For example – if you need a new tyre for your car, instead of writing 'buy new tyre', write down the Active Steps to buying a new tyre, bearing in mind you want to find the best price available to you. This might be – 'yellow pages/phone tyre companies for quotes/order tyre/arrange pick up time.'
- ✓ Have the notebook displaying your **'to do' list for 'today'** at all times, written at the front of the notebook. This will help remind you what you need to get done and also make it easy for you to add to the list.

2) Projects (at back)
- ✓ Keep a list of any ongoing work, home or creative **projects** you have on the go, at the back of the notebook.
- ✓ Designate a **small number of pages** per project.
- ✓ **Write down** ideas, important information, any Active Steps you need to take, and progress.

> Hugh says:
> Planning to do things in achievable chunks, and then crossing these off a list helps to build confidence – it makes us feel we are regularly achieving small things, which is true.

Buy a notebook: Get yourself a basic reporter's pad from a stationers.

This week

Split the pad into two sections ('to do' list and 'projects'). Keep it somewhere prominent and use it each day.

Keep a calendar

Remember important time or day related events.

Keep it somewhere visible. This will help you do jobs on time and prevent an important date creeping up on you. You could keep it in your kitchen or on your desk.

You can use this to:
- ✓ Remember **birthdays** and **weddings**.
- ✓ Remember **appointments**.
- ✓ Remember **meetings**.
- ✓ Remember **completion dates** for important tasks.

Brief. Wherever possible, keep the content you put on your calendar as brief as possible.

Time and day. Only put time and day related reminders on there for important tasks.

Don't clutter. Try and prevent filling up the calendar with too much of your everyday 'to do' lists – you have your notebook for that.

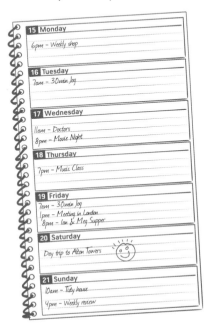

James says:
I'm not sure how, but until recently I didn't have a calendar or a diary. I now have an up-to-date calendar and try not to miss friends' birthdays.

Buy a calendar: Again, you can find a basic one from any stationers.

This week

Once you have a calendar, write down all your important dates and put it somewhere visible, preferably in the kitchen.

Carry out a weekly review

Keep on top of your system with 30 minutes a week.

Daily update. Try to carry out items in your 'to do' lists daily, as well as file paperwork away into your filing system. Keeping on top of your various jobs, projects, appointments and filing is a continual process.

Weekly service. But, like a tidy home or a profitable business, in order to keep your 'organised system' working for you, you also need to service it regularly. Try carrying out a 30 minutes review each week, possibly on a Sunday.

Your weekly review can be helpful in the following ways:
- ✓ **File away** any un-filed material.
- ✓ **Check your calendar** for appointments; planning *when* you will have time to work on one or more of your projects and *what* you will be doing.
- ✓ **Write yourself a 'to do' list** for the week ahead so you feel prepared.

Making the time to do this helps to ensure your calming 'organised system' doesn't become a stressful 'disorganised system'.

Completing your weekly review means you can start the week feeling organised and prepared.

James says:
I'm not a big fan of Monday mornings, to be honest. Getting out of bed and on with the start of a new week feels easier having done my weekly review on the Sunday, though. It leaves me feeling calm, in control and ready!

Carry out a weekly review: Plan a set time to do this each week (possibly on a Sunday). Write it on your calendar.

This week

Carry out your weekly review to stay on top of your home systems so that you start your week feeling organised. You can also do this at work.

Getting started on Step 13...

...Today, tomorrow and this week: Plan a visit to the stationers and a couple of hours 'sorting' at home. You'll need to make sure you have a notebook, a calendar and some coloured files if you don't already have some . Once you have these you can tackle the first three Active Steps in whichever order you want. Enjoy doing the filing as thoroughly as possible and make the writing in your notebook and calendar as clear as possible – this will help you want to, and be able to, keep up your 'system'. Make sure you write in your calendar when you will carry out your weekly review (and then do it when you have planned to!). Being organised and keeping organised will help you feel calm.

Isha

Isha

Our place used to be completely disorganised. Bills and paperwork were stuffed in drawers and post-it notes were scattered around the house to remind me what I needed to buy and do. I had a diary but rarely looked in it so we tended to forget important dates.

It's with great relief that I can say that things are now a lot better. I have all our household paperwork in distinct and separate files. We have them for our different bills and household correspondence – but also for stuff of personal interest. Ian likes to collect cartoons out of newspapers and information on wine, so he has files for each of these. I've even started one up with ideas and cuttings for flower-arranging (for when I get around to doing a course). I also have a separate one marked 'presents' for ideas and offers I have found for different birthday and Christmas gifts for people. I don't put ideas for Ian's presents in there, even though I'm not sure he's found the file yet!

In fact, I feel much better prepared for birthdays in general now. I've got a big calendar that I keep in the kitchen with all our family and friends' birthdays on it. I keep appointments on there too. It's better for me than a diary because it's always hanging up and open so I can check each day what events are coming up. Now, whenever I see there's a birthday coming up some time in the next month I consult my file for inspiration and start planning. I'm not forgetting people's birthdays like before, plus the presents are better!

I still use post-its occasionally, but not as much as before. I use a notebook now to keep track of what jobs need doing each day. It's good having one place to refer to. I can check back over previous days to make sure everything that needs to have been done has been finished and crossed off the list. I also use the back of the notebook to keep track of ideas I have. It sounds silly saying this – but sometimes I have flashes of inspiration that I feel I must record! Occasionally I write down a quote or just a random thought. I also keep a list of music I'd like to buy, films I think Ian and I would like to see and have a separate page marked 'flower-arranging' for any 'flowery ideas' I have! If nothing else, it helps remind me that I want to do a course. I will get around to it!

Getting more organised has helped me to feel more relaxed and in control of what needs to be done. I trust my system and know that as long as I stick to it, review and maintain it, it will work for me. It doesn't feel a chore, either. It's a routine that I enjoy, strangely enough. I also enjoy keeping track of all my interests. I no longer forget the name of the song I hear or film that gets a good review on the radio.

Step 14 Manage your time

Time can often seem to be in short supply. We want to get things done as fast as possible and move on to what's next.

However, despite increased opportunity to complete tasks quicker (through the internet, by phone or by delegation), we still often feel that we don't have time left over in which to stop and think, or enjoy a sense of achievement.

Our partners, colleagues and bosses can reinforce this by subtly or blatantly pointing out what we *haven't* done rather than their acknowledgement of what we *have* done.

There is a lot of evidence that poor time management is a significant problem in the workplace, with 20% of time lost in non-essential or wasted tasks. This must be equally true at home.

There are several methods you can try to improve your own time management and minimise the stress of 'the rush'.

The topics to help you manage your time better are:
- ✓ Prepare more.
- ✓ Reduce procrastination.
- ✓ Release time.
- ✓ Allow enough time.
- ✓ Prioritise your tasks.
- ✓ Say no (sometimes).

Prepare more

Don't let big tasks creep up on you.

Getting started. We often leave preparing properly until it's too late because we are nervous of starting.

Time vs. task. We can end up leaving it *so* late that we end up becoming more stressed about time than the task itself, which may turn out to be easy.

So, how can you prepare more?
- ✓ **At the start of each week,** be proactive and work out what needs to be done at work and at home.
- ✓ **Use your notebook or calendar** (if it's time or day related) to write a list of what needs to be done.
- ✓ **Stay one step ahead** of important deadlines, meetings or events and prepare early for them.
- ✓ **How much** time will you need? **When** will you be able to do this? Don't leave it until the last minute!
- ✓ **At the start of each day,** spend a few minutes planning your day.
- ✓ **Get into the habit** of thinking what the first Active Step is for each job – this will make starting them easier.

Think of preparation as a good idea to do a better job and keep in control of stress.

Hugh says:
I have one list of 'jobs to do' for work and one for home. If the lists are long I will usually work out how much time each job will take and put down when I hope to do them. This makes the list manageable and I feel more in control of getting them done.

AS

Prepare more: What up-and-coming tasks or events do you have over the next week that might require some preparation? Write these down below.

Tasks and events I have this week that require preparation:

....

....

....

....

This week

Allow yourself some time to start your preparation.

Reduce procrastination

Only touch once.

'The put off'. We all occasionally put off jobs that we find difficult or boring. If there is no immediate pressure to complete them, it can be easy to 'add them to the list' of other unfinished tasks.

'The build up'. Letting these build up, however, can sometimes get on top of you and, in turn, lead to a build-up of stress.

Start getting into the habit of:
- ✓ Opening.
- ✓ Reading.
- ✓ Replying/paying.
- ✓ Filing away.

Straightaway any of the following that you receive:
- ✓ Letters.
- ✓ Emails.
- ✓ Texts.
- ✓ Bills.
- ✓ Other correspondence.

Try not to put things off.

Adopting the mantra 'only touch once' can help you to do this.

Once it's in your hands – deal with it.

Only touch paperwork once: Do you have any unopened letters or emails? Or any calls or texts that you haven't replied to? Deal with them now.

This week

Adopt the *only touch once* approach with emails, letters and bills from now on. Once you have opened them, deal with them and file them away immediately.

Release time

Take some pressure off: create more time.

Unfulfilling time. How much extra time, and therefore productivity, would you have if you *wasted* less time?

Fulfilling time. Get rid of time-wasting habits and concentrate on what's most important, effective and fulfilling.

Think of how many hours a week you could 'gain' by cutting down on:
- Looking for items in a disorganised way.
- Time spent shopping.
- Watching excessive amounts of TV.
- Surfing the net for hours on end.
- Being in the pub.

Create an extra 52 days a year. For example – if you watch TV from 6.30pm till 10.30pm, 5 days a week, play computer games for 2 hours a week, and surf the net for 2 hours a week, that's a total of 24 hours or ONE WHOLE DAY per week that you could be spending doing something else more constructive and fulfilling.

What worthwhile activity could you do with any extra time you could make available?:
- ✓ You could be taking **more exercise.**
- ✓ You could be spending more time with **family or friends.**
- ✓ You could put in a little **overtime** at work (not too much!).
- ✓ You could learn another **language.**
- ✓ You could learn how to play a **musical instrument.**
- ✓ You could work on **creative pursuits.**
- ✓ You could have more time to **relax** properly.

How would making progress on this activity (or activities) make you feel?

You may find that you'd get more out of it than you would from the equivalent time spent on the TV and computer.

What could you do with the extra time you could create?

James says:
I find that TV can be quite an addictive pastime as it allows you to switch off mentally and physically. I try to limit the amount I watch now and use the time doing things that challenge and fulfil me more. The TV is still there when there's something good on, or I'm just too tired to do anything else.

Release time: How could you release time? Write down below one unrewarding activity you could cut down on this week.

One unrewarding activity I could reduce this week:

....

This week

Have a go at reducing the time you spend on this activity and replace it with something more fulfilling.

Allow enough time

You only have 24 hours in the day.

Avoid constant rushing. **Allow yourself enough time to complete tasks.**

Be realistic. **You only have 24 hours in the day (including sleep), so be realistic as to how much you can accomplish without getting too stressed.**

Buffer. **Wherever possible, give yourself a little more time than you need to complete a task.**

Remain calm. **Having enough time will help you remain calm.**

Feel good. **Finishing your task early will make you feel good.**

Don't expect to produce miracles every day.

James says:
Setting myself unrealistic targets about getting things done can make me feel frustrated with myself and my day. It's a balance between pushing myself with healthy stress and being realistic and remaining calm.

AS

Allow enough time: Write down below the tasks you have left to do today or that you have for tomorrow and how long each one will take. Have you got enough time to complete them properly?

Task   Time

....

....

....

....

....

....

....

This week

Try writing out what tasks or jobs you have to do at the start of each day and how long you will allow to finish each one. Make sure you give yourself sufficient time.

Prioritise your tasks

Cut down on multi-tasking.

'The juggle'. We can often find ourselves trying to juggle several jobs at once either at home or at work.

Simple tasks. It's fine to do simple tasks whilst you are 'on hold' on a telephone call.

Complicated tasks. More complicated tasks deserve your full attention, though.

Avoid errors and stress. To keep your thinking clear and focussed, try to only attempt one task at a time. You should find that you get things completed quicker and with fewer mistakes.

Put the tasks in some sort of order – experiment with doing:
a) The easiest, shortest tasks first or
b) The most important, urgent tasks first.

A systematic approach can help you get more done, quicker, with fewer mistakes and less stress!

Hugh says:
I tend to start with the easy things, feel good that I've ticked some of the list and then move on to the difficult, longer ones.

Prioritise your tasks: Prioritise the list from the previous topic, starting with either the easiest or the most important tasks first.

Prioritising my list of jobs:

1	6
2	7
3	8
4	9
5	10

This week

Prioritise the tasks on your 'to do' list each day. Do them one at a time and limit multi-tasking wherever possible.

Say no (sometimes)

Remember to be assertive.

Helping out. It is tricky when someone asks for your assistance as it is natural to want to help, and nice to do so.

Under pressure. Of course, in a work environment you may feel obliged to 'say yes' if it is a senior member of the company asking you to do something.

Too much pressure. However, you are permitted to 'say no' to requests from other people if you feel this is putting too much pressure on yourself.

Be assertive. Weigh up the situation based on how much work you have and how you feel.

Compromise. There may be room for a compromise in this situation with the task being completed at a later date or, if appropriate, being delegated to spread the load.

Remember that you also need time to eat, relax and sleep in any given day, as well as complete the tasks you have!

James says:
You'll find that, usually, people will understand if you've got a lot on and would rather you were honest than say you'll do something which you know is unrealistic.

Say no. If you feel you do not have time to carry out one of the jobs on the list you have written above, feel able to 'say no' and remove it from the list.

This week

Think carefully about how much time you have available before accepting extra tasks. Feel able to 'say no' on occasions if you feel you are taking on too much.

Getting started on Step 14...

...Today, tomorrow and this week: Use this step to manage your time better. In the morning, plan thoroughly for the day ahead.

What tasks have you got to do today? What tasks have you got the next day or the day after that may need some early preparation? If possible release some extra time by wasting less and then see what that leaves you with.

Write your list in your notebook, then prioritise the contents before you get started. Remember: manage your time, don't take too much on and feel able to say no.

Isha

Isha

I used to find it difficult to manage my time and get all the things done each day I needed to without getting stressed out in the process. I never seemed to have the time to relax regularly or to focus on the things I wanted to do. It felt like I was fighting a losing battle – I was so disorganised that often it took me all day to do very little. I'd often forget or just put off stuff.

Things are different now. I know that if I work in a more organised and efficient way, I can get more done, remain calmer and have time for myself.

My routine works well. As soon as I get the chance, I sit down with my notebook and calendar at the kitchen table and plan what I want to get done over the course of the day. The amount of time I have available depends on how much work and what appointments I have, of course. But I also need to take into account what's coming up over the next week or so. I try to prepare for things well in advance now if possible – it makes me feel like I'm winning!

I no longer put too much pressure on myself to get things done. I like to deal with all letters or bills first thing and get them out of the way. Late afternoon I sit down and spend 30 minutes replying to emails. Recently Ian has been helping out more in the evenings and weekends.

I now have more time to myself and manage to do my relaxation exercises most evenings or just sit down with a good book or magazine. Oh – apart from Thursdays. That's when I do my flower-arranging course at the local Uni. It's great - I'm so glad I've started. All the newspaper cuttings and notes I've made have come in really handy too.

Behaviour Summary Illustration

Isha has been working on behaviour to reduce stress. She works from, and is also in charge of organising, the family home as her partner Ian works long hours. It's Monday and Isha has a busy week ahead.

1) First thing

Isha uses her calendar to see what's coming up this week. She notices that it's her friend's birthday soon and that she has an important deadline on Friday for work. She writes herself a to-do list in her notebook and then prioritises her tasks.

2) Deal with the post

After breakfast, Isha opens up the day's post. She takes a couple of minutes to deal with a bill and then puts the paperwork into separate files straight away so that she only needs to touch them once. Now it's time for work.

3) Lunch

Before lunch she uses systematic relaxation to make her feel calmer before she sits down to eat. To save money, Isha makes the most of the leftovers from the weekend.

5) Time to herself

Isha decides to **release time** by not watching any TV this evening. Instead of watching TV, she looks through her birthday file to find an idea for her friend's birthday. She knows it will help her feel calm and in control.

4) At the shops

It's late afternoon and Isha takes her weekly budget out in cash to last the rest of the week. She heads to the supermarket. Isha has already **prepared** a plan of what meals they will eat this week and written a shopping list. She knows that having a shopping list and carrying cash will help her save time and **save money**.

6) Relax

Isha relaxes properly before bed. She has a bath, does a **PMR** exercise and then goes to bed with a milky drink and to read. She is pleased to have had such a good day.

Summary: Behaviour to reduce stress

The practical behavioural ideas in this section will really help you to keep a check on your stress levels. As before, take a week now to put into practice the different topics. Make sure you have a go at all the *AS* first; you can then progress with the suggestions we make for *this week*.

Relax more

Put your current ability to relax into more use.
Use the instant relaxation method every day.
Practise systematic relaxation.
Use PMR when you have 20 minutes to relax fully and deeply.
Let go of unproductive anger.

Handle your finances

Monitor your day-to-day spend.
Work out your bills.
Work out your income.
Work out what weekly expenditure you can afford.
Work out what ways you can save money.
Put some money away.

Organise your system

Sort out your paperwork into separate files.
Buy a notebook to use for your 'to do' and 'projects' lists.
Use a calendar for all time or day related reminders.
Carry out a weekly review of your system.

Manage your time

Prepare fully for up-and-coming tasks or events.
Don't procrastinate – adopt the 'only touch once' approach.
Release time by reducing the time you spend on unfulfilling activities.
Don't try to do too much.
Prioritise the tasks you have to do.
Be prepared to 'say no' to tasks that you feel may cause unnecessary stress.

Section 6 Personal action plan to reduce stress

The story so far:
You have read about steps towards reducing stress in areas of your thinking, lifestyle, communication and behaviour. We hope you have made a start, experimenting with the Active Steps and found that they are helpful.

The next phase:
This is to put the Active Steps into regular use for immediate and long-lasting benefits.

How? This involves:
- ✓ **Remembering** what the Active Steps are.
- ✓ **Wanting** to put them into practice.
- ✓ **Having a plan** for doing them.

To help you achieve this, these are the topics in this section:
- ✓ **Summary** of steps and Active Steps.
- ✓ **Prioritise, plan & persist.**
- ✓ **Review** your progress.

We will provide you with helpful advice to get the most out of this section.

Remember what you got from the motivation section, what you learnt about your own stress and what goals you set yourself.

As you start to use more of the stress-busting skills in this book, you will become more confident to manage day-to-day stress. It's a bit like the Samurai swordsman who spends time learning the first sword stroke, then goes on to the second, and so on…. At the end he puts them all together and becomes someone who is ready for battle…. that's you soon!

i) Summary of steps and Active Steps

Here's a summary of all the steps and Active Steps from each of the TLCB sections.

We hope you will recognise most of them.

There are columns on the right hand side where you can note which of the *AS* you have tried out and whether or not you found them helpful.

You can also write your own thoughts and comments underneath if you want.

The summaries of the first two steps feature what you have written on your affirmation card in bold. Continue to use your affirmation card as regularly as you can – it will help you to think positively and logically.

Use this as a reference point for all the different stress-busting approaches in the book, which ones you have found helpful and which ones you have yet to try.

Step 1 **Think positively**   TRIED   HELPFUL

AS Be more confident (p45) about your own ability to get
your next task done. Say to yourself, *'I can do it'* regularly.   ☐   ☐

AS Be more optimistic (p47) about your next task, and about
your day and your week. Think to yourself, *'today is going
to be a good day'* regularly.   ☐   ☐

AS Focus on the positives (p49). Remember to focus on the
positives today, even (and especially) if you are feeling a
little down or stressed. Think of some of the good things
about yourself and what you have done today. Remind
yourself by thinking to yourself, *'focus on the positives'*
regularly.   ☐   ☐

AS Be assertive: express yourself (p52). Make clear 'I
statements' about what you think, feel and want today.
Think to yourself, *'be assertive and express yourself'* to
help you remember.   ☐   ☐

AS Recognise your success (p55). Regularly take some time
today to recognise your successes, especially the small
things.   ☐   ☐

AS Reassure yourself (p57) today in everything you do. Be
your own best friend – supportive and caring. Remind
yourself by thinking, *'be my own best friend'* regularly.   ☐   ☐

AS Watch your negative thoughts (p58) today. Monitor your
thinking for any negative thoughts you may be having.
Challenge them and change them to more positive,
productive ones. Use your affirmation card to help remind
you to do this by saying, *'identify, challenge and change
negative thoughts'* regularly to yourself.   ☐   ☐

Your own thoughts:

....

....

....

....

....

....

....

....

Step 2 **Think logically** TRIED HELPFUL

AS Be specific: don't exaggerate (p63). Talk about specific actions that people take and aspects of situations rather than whole people and whole situations. Think regularly to yourself *'be specific: don't exaggerate.'*

AS Make positive predictions, don't catastrophise (p64). Make positive predictions about your day today, both in your thoughts and when speaking to people. Do this about any work, journeys, meetings or activities you have coming up. Tell yourself *'my day will go well if I think logically.'*

AS Face facts (p66). Face up to any health, wealth or happiness issues you have today. Use your problem-solving skills to help you work out the best approach.

AS Feel good about yourself (p67). Use walking through any doorway today as a trigger for you to think positive thoughts about yourself – keep your head up, breathe in and think *'I'm a good person.'* Get into the habit of saying positive things to yourself regularly.

AS Use problem-solving techniques (p70). Apply the 6-step problem-solving plan to any problems you are faced with. This can help you to face facts and confront the health, wealth and happiness issue(s) from earlier.

AS Understand others' actions (p72). Try to understand and be considerate of how the people around you are feeling. If you sense that they may be worried, upset or stressed about something, offer your support.

AS Don't overreact emotionally (p73). Recognise your feelings and don't let your emotions affect the way you treat people today. Take a deep breath and pause before saying something big or definite. Remind yourself by thinking *'don't overreact emotionally'* as regularly as you can. ☐ ☐

AS Distract yourself (p74) from any anxious or negative thoughts you have today. Use positive thoughts or actions to help you do this. ☐ ☐

AS Have an open mind (p76). Question any preconceptions you have about other people and their different thoughts, beliefs and culture. Accept and be interested in the differences you see in people; don't disregard or be fearful of them. Remind yourself to *'keep an open mind'*. ☐ ☐

AS Watch your illogical thoughts today (p78). Challenge your illogical thoughts and change them to more logical, productive ones. Think to yourself regularly *'identify, challenge and change illogical thoughts'*. ☐ ☐

Your own thoughts:

....

....

....

....

....

Step 3 Imagine calmness

TRIED   HELPFUL

AS Use calm imagery (p82). If you feel you are getting a little worked up today, take a couple of deep breaths and use your favourite calm imagery to relax you.

☐   ☐

AS Visualise success (p84). Visualise yourself successfully completing tasks that lie ahead of you today, large or small.

☐   ☐

AS Use motivation imagery (p85). Throughout today, visualise what it would be like to feel calmer and more in control, to help motivate you to achieve it.

☐   ☐

Your own thoughts:

....

....

....

....

....

....

....

Step 4 Practise mindfulness   TRIED   HELPFUL

AS Focus on your breathing (p91). Regularly throughout today, stop, sit comfortably and focus on your breathing. Breathe in and out slowly and deeply to allow yourself to relax. You can do this wherever you are.

AS Choose productive thoughts (p93). Choose to let go of, and ignore stressful, unproductive thoughts. Focus on calm, productive thoughts. Feel good about yourself, your relationships and your day.

AS Appreciate your senses (p95). Be more aware of, and enjoy each of your senses regularly today. What can you see, feel, hear, taste and smell now?

AS Practise mindful meditation (p97). Put aside 5 minutes today to sit somewhere quietly and uninterrupted, close your eyes and practise mindful meditation.

AS Be more mindful every day (p99). Throughout today, stay in the moment. Be more aware of the little things that make you happy and enjoy them.

Your own thoughts:

....

....

....

Step 5 Get active   TRIED   HELPFUL

AS Visualise enjoying the benefits of getting active (p110) every time you go for a walk or do any other form of exercise. ☐ ☐

AS Have an active lifestyle (p111). When possible, walk or cycle to work, the shops or to meet people today and tomorrow. ☐ ☐

AS Enjoy regular exercise (p114). Take some form of planned exercise today whether it's a workout at home, a run in the park, a session at the gym or a bit of team sport. ☐ ☐

AS Take relaxation exercise (p116). If you haven't already tried this, look into which one appeals to you most. If you have, take some time out today to practise. ☐ ☐

AS Set your goals and think positively about being active (p118). What's your goal for getting active? Use this to help motivate you to get more active, and enjoy doing so. ☐ ☐

AS Activate your mind: be creative (p120). Plan to spend some time today on a creative pursuit. ☐ ☐

Your own thoughts:

....

....

....

....

Step 6 Eat and drink healthily   TRIED   HELPFUL

AS Eat regularly (p125). Have 3 meals and 2 'mid-snacks' today. What will you have? ☐ ☐

AS Enjoy more home cooking (p128). Plan ahead to cut down on the amount you eat out today and this week. Have you got food at home? ☐ ☐

AS Reduce your intake from 'the red list' today (p130). Which items will you cut down on? ☐ ☐

AS Increase your intake from 'the green list' today (p132). Make sure you have a good supply of 'green list' foods at home. Plan a weekly shop from 'the green list' so that you can enjoy more healthy home cooking and can shop more efficiently. ☐ ☐

AS Enjoy each and every mouthful (p134). Each meal today, make a real point of eating.... very.... slowly.... and.... mindfully. Enjoy each and every mouthful. ☐ ☐

AS Apply the 80:20 principle to your eating today (p136). Aim for no less than 80% of your intake to be from 'the green list' and no more than 20% to be from 'the red list'. ☐ ☐

AS Stop smoking (p138). Reduce your smoking today. Remind yourself of three good reasons for you to do this. ☐ ☐

AS Monitor your alcohol intake today (p141). Make sure your intake this week is within the recommended limit, for women (14 units) and men (21 units). Plan how you will achieve this. ☐ ☐

Your own thoughts:

....

Step 7 **Create a calm home**   TRIED   HELPFUL

AS De-clutter your home today (p146). Decide on one room
to start with and be ruthless! If this feels good, schedule to
de-clutter another room too.   ☐   ☐

AS Clean your home (p148). Set aside a 30 minute period to
do this. Put some of your favourite music on as you go and
plan to do something fun after you have finished.

AS Buy some greenery for your home (p149). Visit your local
garden centre today and get yourself an attractive plant for
your home. Where is your local garden centre and what
would you like to get?   ☐   ☐

AS Apply calming finishing touches to your home (p151). Use
relaxing music, joss-sticks and candles to create as calm a
home environment as possible this evening.   ☐   ☐

Your own thoughts:

....

....

....

....

....

Step 8 Balance your lifestyle   TRIED   HELPFUL

AS Balance out the time you work, rest and play (p155).
Leave work at work and spend some time actively and
some time relaxing today.

☐   ☐

AS Get into a good sleeping pattern tonight (p157). Work out
what time you need to get up in the morning and then
go to bed tonight at an hour that gives you enough sleep.
Make sure you relax before bed. Try and go to bed at the
same time the following night.

☐   ☐

AS Have a regular routine but experiment with change (p159).
Plan a routine for today, trying out as many of the stress-
busting ideas as possible. At the same time experiment
with a new activity, journey or destination.

☐   ☐

Your own thoughts:

....

....

....

....

....

Step 9 Communicate clearly

TRIED   HELPFUL

AS Make initial connections today (p172). Whenever you get the chance, smile and say 'hello' to people. How do they react? ☐ ☐

AS Keep conversations going (p174). In the next conversation you have, practise using basic communication skills to keep conversations going. Your conversation should last longer and you should feel more confident in your ability to connect with people. ☐ ☐

AS Share an interest (p175). Practise thinking what you share in common with people rather than how different you are. In your next conversation, talk about interests that you think you share. ☐ ☐

AS Help conversations deepen (p177). Reflect feelings, meanings and try clarifying what has happened when you are next talking to a member of your family, a friend or acquaintance. ☐ ☐

AS Make your 50% contribution worthwhile (p179). Make the next conversation you have today worthwhile. Try to make your contribution as close to 50% as possible. ☐ ☐

Your own thoughts:

....

....

....

Step 10 Exchange positivity and warmth TRIED HELPFUL

AS Seek support (p183). Call someone if you feel stressed, angry or upset today. Who will you call?

☐ ☐

AS Help reassure others (p184). Help reassure family, friends or colleagues today. Share ideas that work.

☐ ☐

AS Resolve differences (p186). Take the first step today to resolve any recent or past differences you may have with someone, or contact someone you haven't spoken to for a while.

☐ ☐

AS Spread positivity and warmth today (p188). Call one family member and one friend today to say hello and see how they are, using your positive communication skills.

☐ ☐

Your own thoughts:

....

....

....

....

....

....

Step 11 Relax more | TRIED | HELPFUL

AS You can relax already (p200). Feel confident that you are good at relaxing and put into practice your current ability to relax more often today.

AS Use instant relaxation (p201) to relax you frequently today. You can do it wherever you are. Why not try it now?

AS Practise systematic relaxation (p203). Make time to try this 10-minute method today. Where and when will you do it?

AS Use PMR (p204). Make time to listen to the PMR CD. This will take 20 minutes.

AS Let go of unproductive anger (p206). If you feel yourself getting angry today, tell yourself to 'stop' and follow the 5-step anger management plan.

Your own thoughts:

....

....

....

....

....

....

Step 12 **Handle your finances**   TRIED   HELPFUL

AS Monitor your day-to-day spending (p212). If you haven't done so already, buy yourself a small notebook so you can start monitoring how much you spend, and on what.   ☐   ☐

AS Work out your bills (p214). Add up all your yearly bills to give you a weekly or monthly figure.   ☐   ☐

AS Work out your income (p215). Add up your yearly income (after tax), and divide it to give you a weekly or monthly figure.   ☐   ☐

AS Work out what weekly day-to-day expenditure you can afford (p216). Subtract weekly bills from weekly income.   ☐   ☐

AS Save money (p218). Try reducing money you spend on energy, food and drink, luxury goods and travel today. Carry a small amount of cash on you instead of 'plastic'.   ☐   ☐

AS Set up a new savings account today (p221) and/or buy yourself a 'piggy bank' for home.   ☐   ☐

Your own thoughts:

....

....

....

....

Step 13 **Organise your systems**   TRIED   HELPFUL

AS Sort out your paperwork (p226) into distinct files with
clear labels.

AS Buy a notebook (p227) if you haven't already done so.
Split it into two sections ('to do' list and 'projects'); keep it
somewhere prominent and start using it.

AS Buy a calendar (p228) if you don't already have one. Input
all your important dates and put it somewhere visible.

AS Carry out a weekly review (p230). Plan a set time to do
this each and every week. Write it on your calendar now.

Your own thoughts:

....

....

....

....

....

....

....

Step 14 Manage your time   TRIED   HELPFUL

AS Prepare more (p234). Check what up-and-coming tasks or events you have today and over the next week. Begin any necessary preparation today.

☐   ☐

AS Only touch paperwork once (p235). Adopt this approach with emails, letters and bills. Once you have opened them, deal with them and file them away, if possible – straight away.

☐   ☐

AS Release time (p237). Reduce the amount of time you spend on unfulfilling activities today, replacing it with something more fulfilling.

☐   ☐

AS Allow enough time (p239). Write down the tasks you have left to do today and how long each one will take. Have you got enough time to complete them properly?

☐   ☐

AS Prioritise your tasks (p241). Work through the tasks you have left to do today, either in order of importance or easiest first. Do them one at a time and limit 'multi-tasking' wherever possible.

☐   ☐

AS Say no (p242). Think carefully about how much time you have available before accepting another task today. Feel able to 'say no'.

☐   ☐

Your own thoughts:

....

....

ii) Prioritise, plan & persist

On getting this far in the book, we hope you have had a go at each step and some of their **AS**. This is designed to give you a taster of how each of these steps can make you feel.

For example, having practised one or two different ways to relax physically and mentally, you will feel more confident that you can bring on a feeling of relaxation wherever you are.

Having organised your systems and filed or thrown away your old bills, letters and general papers, it will feel great to be more in control of all your paperwork. Using a notebook to plan with, and a calendar to keep track of important dates, will further enhance this feel-good factor. You will be confident that you are more organised and won't forget things.

It is now a process of maintaining your focus and progress on each of the 14 steps.

For this to happen, we want you to find an approach that helps you to stay with the positive changes you have made, and are making.

After all, to maintain long-lasting benefits of stress management and increased calmness, and to achieve your goals, you need to see the steps we talk about in this book as long-term approaches, not just ideas to try briefly and then gradually forget about.

It is now a case of putting plans in place to help you incorporate all the steps into your weekly schedule. They need to become part of your routine, habits and 'everyday actions'.

This part of the book looks at:
- ✓ Prioritising getting calmer.
- ✓ Plan 1: The reactive calming plan.
- ✓ Plan 2: The proactive calming plan.
- ✓ Persisting with the 14 steps.

Prioritising getting calmer

Make it your priority to become a calmer person.

Make it your priority to plan for and persist with the 14 steps.

Practise being aware of your TLCB – remember this means your thinking, lifestyle, communication and behaviour. Is it positive, productive and calming?

Try to reduce negative approaches, focussing instead on the positives ones.

For example, get into the habit of regularly listening to your thoughts. Identify any negative, pessimistic and illogical thoughts; challenge them to see if they are really true or helpful. If they are not – change them to more positive, optimistic and logical thoughts.

Make an agreement with yourself now by saying, 'I will prioritise the 14 steps and become a calmer person.'

Make an agreement with yourself now by saying, 'I will...':
- ✓ Think positively and optimistically.
- ✓ Think logically and constructively.
- ✓ Use calm, positive imagery.
- ✓ Be more mindful of my senses.
- ✓ Eat and drink more healthily.
- ✓ Have a more active day-to-day lifestyle.
- ✓ Create a clean, uncluttered and calm home.
- ✓ Balance the amount of time I work, rest and play.
- ✓ Communicate clearer with friends, family and even strangers.
- ✓ Be warmer and more positive to people.
- ✓ Relax deeper and more often.
- ✓ Gain better control of my finances.
- ✓ Organise my home and work systems.
- ✓ Use my time more productively.

Remember - you are creating more time for yourself by reducing the amount of time you waste on unfulfilling activities, by becoming more time efficient in what you do, AND these steps don't take up too much time *anyway*. You can achieve each and every one of the above statements.

Having read the list on p269, you will realise how much you know about managing your own stress.

Plan 1: The reactive calming plan

The first of your personal action plans is *the reactive calming plan*.

This plan is to help with events which *we typically experience every day*. These include conversations with people, situations at work or home and the feelings we encounter along the way whether they be positive, negative or neutral.

We can't control these events from happening. However, the fact that we know they will happen, means that we can predict them to a certain extent. Once they happen, we can use our skills to manage them.

This plan is about using all ideas that you know about and have tried already. It is about applying your new TLCB techniques more and more in your everyday life – helping you deal with situations confidently in a calm, positive and effective manner.

You probably already do this to some extent, and we hope there are some new ideas here too. It's all about applying the ideas in this book into everyday life more and more frequently.

We have written below some common everyday events as well as suggestions of which *AS* you can use to react and remain calm. The page numbers alongside refer to where in the book you can find out more on each of the *AS*. The idea is to see the reactive plan (and the *AS* that make it up) as examples of how to use the ideas in this book when necessary.

You are meeting someone for the first time

Be confident (p45). Reassure yourself that you can handle the situation and get on well with whomever you meet. Have an open mind (p76). Try not to judge someone based on how they look, speak or where they are from. Make initial connections (p172). Get off to a good start by maintaining eye contact, smiling and exchanging greetings. Keep the conversation going (p174). Use your conversational skills such as turning towards the other person, listening and asking short questions to keep the conversation going.

You have a telephone conversation with a friend

Share an interest (p175). Talk about something you know you are both interested in. Help the conversation deepen (p177). If your friend is expressing how they feel about something, try to understand them. Help reassure others (p184). Help them to feel good about themselves and reassure them that things will be OK, where appropriate. Spread positivity and warmth (p188). Generally be as positive and optimistic as you can – try to have a laugh too!

You get into a debate with someone

Be assertive: express yourself (p52). Don't be afraid to say what you think and feel. Keep an open mind (p76). Be open to what the other person is saying. Make your 50% contribution worthwhile (p179). Don't be too overpowering by the amount or 'strength' of what you say.

You have an argument

Let go of unproductive anger (p206). Follow the 5-step anger management plan. Focus on the positives (p49). Remember the good things about the person with whom you have had the argument with. Reassure yourself (p57). Don't give yourself a hard time, reassure yourself that things will work out. Understand others' actions (p72). Try to understand the other person rather than just automatically dismissing them and their point of view. Resolve differences (p186). Take the first step to resolve any differences.

You have a busy day ahead

Be confident (p45). Tell yourself in a confident inner voice that you can cope with the day ahead. Be optimistic (p47). Tell yourself that the day will go well. Prioritise your tasks (p241). Work through them without multi-tasking. Use instant relaxation (p201). Do this frequently throughout the day to relax you. Say no (p242). Feel able to say no to extra jobs.

You have a difficult task

Make positive predictions (p64). Predict success in your own thoughts and when speaking to others. Use problem-solving techniques (p70). Stay calm and apply the 6-step problem solving plan. Use coping imagery (p84). Visualise yourself successfully completing the task. Seek support (p183). Talk to someone if you feel you need help or support.

You make a mistake

Reassure yourself (p57). Don't give yourself a hard time, talk positively to yourself. Focus on the positives (p49). What have you done well today? Distract yourself (p74). Get on with your next job, call a friend or just take a break.

You feel upset

Use problem-solving techniques (p70). Work out why you feel upset and what you can do about it – use the 6-step plan. Seek support (p183). If you are still upset call someone for a chat. Enjoy regular exercise (p114). Go for a brisk walk to burn up any stressful adrenalin and to clear your head. Practise systematic relaxation (p203). Allow yourself five to ten minutes to use this great relaxation technique.

You've been having difficulty sleeping

Reduce items from 'the red list' (p130). Cut down on caffeinated drinks, tobacco and alcohol before bed. Enjoy regular exercise (p114). Try to fit in some form of exercise each day, even if it is just a walk around the block in the evening. Use PMR (p204). Take twenty minutes to relax deeply and fully listen to the CD. Choose productive thoughts (p93). Think positive, calm and productive thoughts before bed. Get into good sleeping patterns (p157). Get into a routine of regularly going to bed and getting up at the same times. This is reactive and proactive – try to get into the habit of doing this all the time.

A friend is upset
Prioritise your tasks (p241). Make time to phone a friend or, better still, to see them. Understand others' actions (p72). Try to put yourself in their shoes to empathise with how they feel. Help reassure others (p184). Your friend will appreciate your support and you will feel good for being there. Inject genuine positive comments about the friend and his or her situation where possible.

You need to go somewhere local
Have an active lifestyle (p111). Try to walk or cycle to your destination to get some exercise. Appreciate your senses (p95). Enjoy the sounds, smells and sights along the way. Visualise enjoying the benefits of being active (p110). Feel good about making active choices and visualise the benefits you will gain.

You are driving in heavy traffic
Choose productive thoughts (p93). Focus on calm and positive thoughts rather than allow yourself to get worked up. Use calm imagery (p82). Take a few deep breaths and visualise something or somewhere that relaxes you. Use instant relaxation (p201). Take a few seconds to relax physically, not taking your eyes off the road!

You have a free evening in
Apply calming finishing touches (p151). Put on some soothing music and dim the lights. Spread positivity and warmth (p188). Ring a member of your family and a friend to say hello. Do something creative (p120). Spend a bit of time on a fun, creative pursuit. Relax before bed (p157). Have a hot bath and get stuck into a good book.

You feel bored or de-motivated at work
Use motivation imagery (p85). Visualise what you wish to achieve this week or year – how would it feel? Seek support (p183). Speak to a colleague or a friend to discuss how you feel. Have regular exercise (p114). If you get the chance, go for a brisk walk – the fresh air could help clear your mind.

You are thinking about the past negatively

Choose productive thoughts (p93). Try to think logical, calm and productive thoughts. Seek support (p183). Talk things through with someone who cares about you. Focus on the positives (p49). Take some time to think of what's good in your life.

You go for a walk

Appreciate your senses (p95). What can you hear, smell and see? Make initial connections (p172). Where appropriate, smile or say hello to people you see. Be more mindful (p99). Enjoy the moment.

You will find that with practice you can do the following more and more:
- Understand the actions you can take in any given situation to help you feel calm and in control.
- Be aware of how to put these into practice.
- Reduce your feeling of being constrained by your stress or your past difficulties.
- Be more confident in your own abilities.
- Be more optimistic.

Plan 2: The proactive calming plan

The proactive calming plan is made up of ideas taken from this book that you can plan in advance to fit into your weekly schedule.

They are in your control and less due to other people's actions or difficult situations which may arise.

Most of the activities won't take long to do and individually they will all help. Together, and carried out regularly week in week out, they result in even greater benefits.

Think of these as proactive methods of keeping stress at bay.

Your proactive calming plan should include the following activities:
- ✓ Reading your affirmation card (positive and logical thinking).
- ✓ Mindfulness meditation.
- ✓ Systematic relaxation.
- ✓ PMR.
- ✓ Calling family and friends.
- ✓ Maintaining financial control.
- ✓ Preparation for work and tasks.
- ✓ Weekly food shop ('the green list').
- ✓ Having an active lifestyle.
- ✓ Regular exercise and/or relaxation exercise.
- ✓ Creative pursuits.
- ✓ Cleaning, de-cluttering and creating a calm home.
- ✓ Balancing the time you work, rest and play.
- ✓ Weekly review of your system.

As you can see, these are all ideas you have tried already. They are varied and easy to do. As we have said before – the trick to the stress-busting techniques we talk about in this book isn't the knowing that they are a good idea - it's the DOING!

The most important thing now, and from now on is to find a method of putting these ideas into your weekly routine, *every week.*

When do I make a proactive calming plan?
- ✓ A good idea is to take about 15 minutes on a Sunday afternoon to plan when you will fit the activities into your schedule for the next week.
- ✓ Naturally, your plans may change a little over the week, but this will give you a good framework.
- ✓ You can update your plans for each day first thing in the morning (either at work or at home), finalising what you want to achieve in the day ahead.
- ✓ The aim is to maintain a healthy balance between your responsibilities and your *proactive calming plan.*

How do I make a proactive calming plan?

1) Use a diary or notebook as this may be too much information to write on your calendar. You can work out when you will carry out these proactive calming activities over the next week.

2) Set yourself small, achievable targets so that you feel good about reaching them.

3) Fit in calming activities whenever you can. This could be before you go to work in the morning, while at work, during your lunch break, on the way home from work, at home, before bed and other times throughout the day.

4) Remember: it all adds up. Activities such as instant relaxation, calling a friend or going for a walk need only take a minute or two. Even a minute's mindful meditation or deep breathing will help.

Writing down these plans will help you to:
- ✓ Prioritise increasing your personal calmness.
- ✓ Acknowledge what you wish to achieve each week.
- ✓ Not miss out any steps.
- ✓ Manage your time.
- ✓ Remember to carry out your plans, once made.
- ✓ Feel calm and in control about what you have to do.

Below, we have written out how your weekly plan *could* look.

Read the following sample plan and think how your own plan might look:

Monday

Before work	5 min mindfulness meditation; read affirmation card; look at calendar.
First thing at work	Plan day ahead with diary/notebook (assess time needed and available; plan and prioritise).
Lunchtime	Read affirmation card; go for 10 min walk; call a family member or friend; take cash out for weekly spend.
After work	Weekly supermarket shop (from 'green list'); deal with home bills and correspondence (only touch once).
Before bed	Systematic relaxation; read affirmation card; read in bed.

Tuesday

Before work	Read affirmation card; 5 min mindfulness meditation; walk to work or go for 10 min walk.
First thing at work	Plan day ahead.
Lunchtime	Read affirmation card; instant relaxation; call a family member or friend.
After work	Go for a run or planned exercise (i.e. gym).
Before bed	Relaxing bath with aromatherapy oils and candles; read affirmation card.

Wednesday

Before work	Read affirmation card; 5 min mindfulness meditation.
First thing at work	Plan day ahead.
Lunchtime	Read affirmation card; systematic relaxation; call a family member or friend.
After work	Deal with home bills and correspondence (only touch once); tidy home; do something creative.
After dinner	Slow, mindful walk; read affirmation card.

Thursday

Before work	Read affirmation card; 5 min mindfulness meditation; walk to work or go for 10 min walk.
First thing at work	Plan day ahead.
Lunchtime	Read affirmation card; instant relaxation (2 mins).
After work	Go for a run or planned exercise (i.e. gym); call a family member or friend.
Before bed	Instant relaxation (2 mins); read in bed; read affirmation card.

Friday

Before work	Read affirmation card; 5 min mindfulness meditation.
First thing at work	Plan day ahead.
Lunchtime	Go for 10 min walk; call a family member or friend.
After work	Deal with home bills and correspondence (only touch once); create a calm home; do some relaxation exercise.
Before bed	Listen to the PMR CD; read affirmation card.

Saturday

Read affirmation card.
5 min mindfulness meditation.
Go for long mindful walk.
Meet up with some friends or family for a catch-up.
Do something creative.

Sunday

Read affirmation card.
5 min mindfulness meditation.
Carry out weekly review of your 'system'.
Tidy home.

The plan we have outlined here is just to give you an idea of how yours could look – you will want to make your own to fit in with your schedule and to include your preferred activities.

Once again, your daily proactive calming plan won't take up too much time because:

* Most of the calming activities don't take long.
* You have planned them in advance.
* You have created more time through better organisation, time management and reduced wasted/unfulfilled time.
* It soon becomes routine.

AND

* You are motivated to carry out the calming activities because you *feel a lot calmer as a result*. And, once you feel calmer you can actually *get more done*.

So, put together your own proactive calming plan. This may just be for the first week (and then redo for subsequent weeks) or may be a routine you can try to keep to each week. We have provided you with blank diary pages at the back of the book (p309). Alternatively, use your own diary, journal or notebook to plan it.

Putting both the *reactive calming plan* and the *proactive calming plan* into action will help you achieve long-lasting calmness and control.

Persisting with the 14 steps

You will now feel far more motivated and confident to carry out your own calmness plans.

Prioritising and planning to become a calmer person is a great start.

Once you get going, PERSIST with the positive approaches that you have started.

Whether you are calm or stressed out, happy or sad, alone or with friends – keep using your positive approaches.

Doing the following will help:
- ✓ Continue to *evaluate* your motivation for the 14 steps.
- ✓ Continue to *experiment* with the 14 steps.
- ✓ Continue *changing* your negative approaches to positive ones.
- ✓ Continue to *prioritise* the 14 steps.
- ✓ Continue to *plan* for the 14 steps.
- ✓ Continue with *all* the 14 steps.
- ✓ Continue with the 14 steps even when you start to feel *calmer.*
- ✓ Continue with the 14 steps even if you feel *stressed out or unhappy.*

Let's look at the last three points in a little more detail:

Persistence means continuing with all the 14 steps

We don't want you to feel bogged down with too much to think about and do. However, persisting with all 14 steps shouldn't be hard work or time-consuming. Why is this important, though?

Each individual step that you master will make a big difference. Neglecting one or more of the 14 steps could reduce your potential for calmness.

Here's three examples of how neglecting a step can reduce your potential for calmness:

1) You persist with all the 14 steps EXCEPT thinking positively (Step 1). Can you become a calmer person if you are not *positive and optimistic*?
2) You persist with all the 14 steps EXCEPT creating a calm home (Step 7). Can you expect to feel calmer if you come home after work to a cluttered and stressful home environment?
3) You persist with all the 14 steps EXCEPT getting a handle on your finances (Step 12). Can you expect to feel calmer if your finances are out of control?

The point we are trying to make here is that although every positive change, every step that you persist with, will help you become calmer – you will be holding yourself back unless you persist with *all 14.*

Neglecting just one could reduce the impact of the other good work you are putting in.

Persistence means continuing with the 14 steps even when you start to feel calmer

It would be very easy, and perhaps quite natural, to stop persisting with the 14 steps once you feel calmer (which is probably already starting to happen). After all, that is what you have set out to achieve, so job done, mission accomplished!

This wouldn't be a great idea, though. After all – the reason you will feel calmer is because you have tried and *continue to practise* the 14 steps.

Use this feeling of increased calmness as reinforcement for the changes you have made and as an incentive to persist with the 14 steps.

Use this feeling of increased calmness as a reason never to get complacent and turn back to old stress-inducing forms of TLCB.

Use it as a stepping-stone to push on and achieve your life goals.

> *Persistence means continuing with the 14 steps even if you feel stressed out or unhappy*

Even if you follow this book to the last letter, you are still going to encounter stressful or unhappy feelings occasionally. We all do.

However, when this happens you have two choices: either make the stress worse with negative approaches, or manage your stress in the short-term and reduce it in the long-term with positive, calming approaches.

Don't let these 'episodes' throw you. Use simple techniques like instant relaxation, phoning a friend or going for a walk to help return you to a calmer state.

For further assistance, we have also given you action plans for four typical stressful events in the Appendix on p291.

These are:
- ✓ Action plan for overload.
- ✓ Action plan for a new situation.
- ✓ Action plan for a negative event.
- ✓ Action plan for a crisis.

These plans will give you some ideas on how to use your own skills and confidence when faced with any of the above situations. You can refer to one or more of these straight away if and when you find yourself in one of these situations, They will immediately give you some ideas to consider and reassure you about how to cope.

So, prioritise all the 14 steps, plan how you will put them into action, and persist with them. If you do this, you will feel calmer every day.

iii) Review your progress

Different people will find different activities more rewarding and calming.

Find out which ones work best for you after giving *all the AS* a go first.

You may have a preconception about one of the suggested activities which puts you off, yet after trying it, find that the activity is fun and helps to relax you more than you thought it would.

Regularly review how you are getting on with the steps, and also how you are feeling.

This is vital to ensure you are making the progress you wish to be making and fully appreciate it.

Here we will look at:
- ✓ **The weekly review.**
- ✓ **Becoming an expert.**

Weekly review

We discussed earlier taking about 15 minutes on a Sunday to put together your proactive plan for the following week. Before doing this, review the progress you have made over the *previous week* (once you get started).

This will allow you to appreciate benefits and 'tweak' your proactive calming plan to make it as efficient as possible.

So, sit with your journal or some notepaper to carry out your review once a week in conjunction with planning for the *next week*.

Why not have your favourite drink or snack or listen to your favourite music while you carry out your review? You could schedule a favourite hobby or pastime as a reward for when the review is finished.
Of course, you don't have to carry out the review on a Sunday – it could

be at any convenient time during the week. Although Sunday does tend to be a day that most people find less busy.

But, try to ensure it is done *each* week. You can also be mentally reviewing it as you go along.

Carry out the review in the following way:

Ask yourself:

Have you been feeling calm this week? If so, why? Which of the steps and *AS* in particular have been working for you? Try to do more of these next week. For example, you may have started taking more exercise by walking to work and going to the gym twice a week. If you recognise that this is making you feel good, do it next week too.

Ask yourself:

Have you felt stressed this week? If so, why? Can you identify negative approaches that have contributed to this? Try to reduce these next week. For example, you may realise that you have been thinking and talking negatively about yourself and other people. Try next week to change these negative, stressful thoughts into positive, calming ones.

Review the 14 steps:

Which steps have you started this week? Could you do more of the *AS* in these steps?
For example, you may have de-cluttered your home this week, which you have found to be a great relief, but not got around to giving it a good clean. Why not carry out a 'spring clean' next week and add a little calming greenery too? You could set yourself the target of sitting down on Saturday night with a glass of wine, having finished the clean-up, added some greenery and applied the finishing touches with some joss-sticks, candles and relaxing music. If starting this step has made you feel good, finishing it will make you feel even better (next week).

Review the 14 steps:

Which ones have you yet to start? Could you concentrate on one or more of these next week to feel calmer?

For example, you may not have got around to looking at your finances yet because you have been too busy or were just putting it off. You are aware that because you haven't looked at them, and that they may *need* looking at, this is not helping you to feel calm. Schedule in some time to look at your finances in your proactive plan for next week. You will feel better for it in the long run. Start by getting all the necessary papers into one pile and go from there.

Review your motivation:

Remind yourself of why you are trying to reduce stress and become a calmer person. Read Section 1 again (p21-p39).

For example, you may feel you have lost sight of the personal goals that you have set yourself. It is natural that this may happen from time to time. It is good to regularly remind ourselves of what we want to achieve, and why. This helps to re-focus our minds and re-energise our motivation.

This review is an important part of your approach to managing stress.

To prioritise, plan and persist will get you results, but to make the most of these benefits, appreciate what, in particular, works *for you*.

Remember, although each of the 14 steps is important, we are all different and may appreciate the rewards from different steps to different degrees.

Understanding which ones work best for you will help you further understand your relationship with calmness and help you maintain feelings of control, positivity and calmness tomorrow, the next day and into the future.

Become an expert

Throughout this book we have suggested approaches to help you develop a greater confidence, choice and mastery over your response to stress. You will recognise this 'mastery' on an everyday basis in most things you do – at home, at work and in your social and leisure activities.

Your stress management falls into four levels of mastery:

Level 1 – Identification and understanding
At this level, you know about an idea and understand it, but probably don't use it on a regular basis, if at all, but it 'sounds sensible'.

Level 2 - Basic mastery
You can do a step or *AS* if asked to, and occasionally put it into practice, but don't really 'own it'.

Level 3 – Active mastery
Here you use a technique on a frequent and everyday basis, to good effect. It is part of your own 'positivity' now.

Level 4 – Expert mastery
You feel confident you have a choice of stress-reducing techniques and can put them into practice whenever you want. Your best friend comes to you for advice on stress; what do you do? Because you know, understand and use these steps frequently, you can counsel your friends and family, telling them what ideas have worked for you, to help them reduce *their* stress.

As you read the book and practise the *AS* frequently, set yourself the target of increased 'mastery', from level 1 through to level 4. Eventually you will find you can use these techniques spontaneously, as they have become *part of you.*

Conclusion: The future you

Congratulations – you've nearly reached the end of the book!

Whether you have read it cover to cover all in one go or have read it in several sittings, we hope you now feel you know a great deal about what stress is, how it affects you, and, most important of all, how you can effectively manage and reduce it.

The calming plans (reactive & proactive) are there to help you continue to put the *AS* into practice for long-lasting benefits.

We would like to remind you of some of the key success factors which will ensure your progress towards increased calmness.

The key success factors are:
- ✓ Reassure yourself that the ideas in this book will work for you.
- ✓ Be positive and inspired to try *AS* out, persist with them and watch what happens.
- ✓ Small changes you make to your TLCB will add up for long-term improvements in how you feel.
- ✓ Notice the benefits you feel – they will help motivate you to keep going.
- ✓ Get help and support from your relatives, friends and colleagues by letting them know what you are trying to do.

We hope you are feeling excited about the benefits you are going to experience in the future by carrying out the ideas in this book.

Practise being enthusiastic about what you do – sometimes this comes naturally and sometimes it needs conscious effort. Either way, allow yourself more and more to feel enthusiastic and positive.

You will feel some improvements as soon as you start, but it is also important to think of your personal journey to increased calmness as just that: a journey, a process; something that you will need to persist with to gain maximum reward. It's like climbing a ladder, slowly upwards, step-by-step.

Let's explain this analogy further.

When people are unhappy or in trouble they often talk about being 'in a hole'. Likewise, when overloaded we often say we 'can't see the wood for the trees'. These sayings are descriptive of the way stress can make us feel: trapped within our own anxiety and tension, unable to think or act logically in order to see how to move forwards positively.

In contrast to that, we say that we can see clearly when we are calm and in control. Calmness allows us the vision to know *where we are now*, *where we would like to be* and *how best to make that journey*. It offers us the control and confidence to help make this journey easier and the chance to fulfil more of our goals.

Think of the ideas in this book as your ladder to climb out of the 'stress hole' and up to the height of calmness, where you will be able to 'see clearly' how to proceed with YOUR journey.

You may not realise it, but you have already started to climb your ladder. Establishing your own goals has been a great start. Experimenting with different steps and Active Steps has helped you climb the ladder further. Sticking with your own calming plan will see you to the top. What will *you* see from the top – achievable life goals that lie ahead? Who will *'the future you'* be when you feel calmer?

More and more, you will begin to obtain a clear vision of how you can manage stress and stressful circumstances, relax more deeply and more often, reverse stressful thinking, communicate in a clear and positive way; and do all these things while maintaining a healthy lifestyle.

More and more, you will make a connection between doing these things and feeling calmer, more positive, more optimistic, happier and more in control of your everyday life.

More and more, you will see yourself achieving the emotional goals and life goals that you have set yourself.

CONGRATULATIONS!

At this stage, all there is left for us to do is *congratulate you* for getting this far in the book, to let go of the reins and say *'go for it!'* Keep experimenting with as many of the *AS* as possible and build these techniques into your day to day life.

But, before you carry on along your path to becoming a healthier, happier and calmer person we have one final question for you:

Who is the future you?

Most of us have ambitions relating to how we would like to feel, what we would like to do, what type of relationships we want and what we would like to achieve in the future. You have already established what these are *for you*, earlier in the book.

Now, imagine this: could it be that your existing dreams, ambitions and plans may be just the tip of the iceberg of your true potential, once you become calmer, more positive and more in control?

Your ambition may be to feel calmer; you may imagine how this might feel.
But this feeling could be 10, 100, or 1000 times more rewarding than you think, once you actually feel calmer.

You may visualise things you could be doing in the future, once you are a calmer person.
But who's to say that you won't uncover a hidden talent or skill with all the increased well-being, focus and control you are experiencing?

You may predict how much more rewarding your relationships could be with your partner, family and friends.
Once you feel calmer and more positive, you may find the true worth of the relationships you foster overtakes your predictions.

You can go on to achieve more and more whether that be emotionally, professionally, vocationally, or in your relationships.

Conclusion The future you

These thoughts about our future can motivate us to keep going, but all we can really do is live positively *today*. If we are too preoccupied with 'tomorrow', it may never arrive, the way we would like it to, because we have spent too long dreaming rather than *doing*.

Each new day allows us the opportunity to grow as individuals in how we think, in the lifestyle we have, how we connect with people and in what we do. Each new day allows us to do something positive *now*, take 'the future' into our own hands just a little more, and gradually make our dreams our *reality*.

Paradoxically, the question 'who is the future you?' really means 'what are you doing now?'
If you live positively today, what does tomorrow hold?
If you live positively today and tomorrow, how are you going to feel the day after tomorrow?
All that remains is to do it to find out. If you haven't already done so, why not start *today*?
Be confident and optimistic that you can become a calmer person. Persist with the small positive changes to your TLCB that will come together to give you a calmer way of coping. With persistent practice, you will notice significant benefits.

By following 14 steps, you will start to notice positive change on many different levels:

- ✓ Increased calmness.
- ✓ A sense of well-being and control.
- ✓ Confidence at home and at work.
- ✓ Increased enthusiasm and motivation.
- ✓ A more balanced lifestyle.
- ✓ Feeling healthier and fitter.
- ✓ Building stronger relationships.
- ✓ Success at work.
- ✓ Increased focus on fulfilment of life goals.

So, well done for getting this far in the book.

It's now time for us to wish you good luck and encourage you wholeheartedly to go for it!

We hope you are as excited as we are about the prospect of positive change.

Who is the future you?

Appendix

Other Action Plans

Persisting with your own action plans will help you to feel calmer and more in control. There are still likely to be occasions, however, when you feel stress recurring due to overload, change or negative events.

This part of the book looks at:
  ✓   An action plan for when we feel overloaded.
  ✓   An action plan for an unfamiliar situation or stressful fear.
  ✓   An action plan for an everyday negative event.
  ✓   An action plan for a crisis event.

Action plan for overload

Waking up in the morning to face the day, getting to work and seeing your desk covered in papers, looking at the long list of jobs to do at home, coping with your children's demands – these are everyday situations we all know and…. love? In these or other similar situations we can often feel 'overloaded' and get stressed. This may be temporary, or affect most of our day, or worse, make us feel our life is running away from us and is out of control. So how can we manage overload?

Let's start by defining 'overload':
1) Several practical tasks to be done today, over the next week or month.
2) One or two difficult tasks to be done.
3) One task you don't really want to do, but need to.
4) Pressure from other people to do something or behave in a certain way.
5) Physical or emotional fatigue, usually linked to excessive and unrewarding activity.
6) Lack of task vs. relaxation balance.
7) Insufficient enjoyment from activity.

As a result of experiencing overload, we can feel stressed, worried, low in self-esteem and confidence and also de-motivated and unenthusiastic. This then becomes a vicious cycle, which makes us even less able to address the type of overload we are faced with.

What to do?
We are *all* susceptible to 'overload' in our everyday life. It is therefore a good idea to have a practical approach we are confident of referring to for help when we start to feel under the cosh.

Normalise your view of overload.
Don't think of yourself as silly or inadequate if you find it hard to cope with events at home or work. In many ways, being overloaded is part of being *alive and kicking* and having an active, busy and worthwhile life. In other respects it indicates that you need to look at your TLCB skills to prevent you from feeling too stressed or out of control.

Make a plan: 'manage this beast'.
Your plan will need to be divided into the key areas of your everyday living: your TLCB. To *have a plan* is very necessary and immediately gives you confidence.

1) Your thinking: 'I can sort this'.
As you know, your *thinking* has a huge effect on how you *feel* and how you cope.

Practising the following thoughts will help:
- ✓ I've felt overloaded before and got through it.
- ✓ I can sort out this overload.
- ✓ I need to get organised.
- ✓ However big my list is, if I start at one end, I will get through it bit-by-bit.
- ✓ I will apply problem-solving skills using the 6-step plan.

2) Your lifestyle: Keep your batteries charged.

✓ The temptation may be to skimp on meals, but it is crucial when managing overload to eat and drink healthily. Your fatigue and sleep disturbance when 'too busy' can be reduced by good diet and hydration.

✓ You will be amazed how a 10 – 15 minute bout of moderate exercise such as brisk walking, jogging or cycling can help you burn-up some of the feelings of stress, put your 'overload' in perspective and allow you to think clearly again.

3) Your communication: Express optimism and control to others.

✓ Share your 'issue' with a friend by phone, text or e-mail or face-to-face.

✓ Share your confidence that, despite it being hard, you aim to sort out this 'overload'.

✓ Enlist encouragement and enthusiasm from others rather than sympathy or sorrow.

✓ Build on contact with others as you work through the overload to get further encouragement.

✓ Make sure you communicate your success to them.

4) Your behaviour: Let's get this sorted.

✓ Write a list of what this 'overload' actually is, e.g. a list of jobs, or one big job with a number of tasks.

✓ Subdivide the list into mini-tasks or **AS** in your notebook.

✓ Decide if you can 'say no' to some tasks or if some can be delegated.

✓ Estimate roughly how long each task will take and write this alongside each task (in minutes or hours).

✓ Prioritise which tasks or Active Steps to do first. This could be the easiest or the most difficult, the quickest or the longest.

✓ Decide when you are going to 'attack' this list. You may be able to 'start, keep going and finish' in one session, or you may need to divide it into two or more sessions.

- ✓ If possible, keep the list and the item being dealt with in front of you. Hide or put out of sight the other items for the time being so you only need to focus on the task at hand.
- ✓ As you complete tasks, tick them off your list and, if possible remove from sight or file away the completed items.
- ✓ Even when faced with significant overload, remember to relax by taking occasional deep breaths, and use the instant and systematic relaxation techniques. If you are *physically* more relaxed, you will be more able to *think* more clearly and act more positively.

Be positive in your actions but try not to rush or multi-task. Focus on one task at a time – you will get there in the end.

Prevent future overload.
Each time you have experienced some type of overload, you will have learnt how to cope with it better. The techniques we refer to here can help on future occasions to deal with overload, or in some instances, *prevent* future overload. Use these approaches to build your confidence to manage stressful situations.

Make sure you talk to friends and relatives about this issue so you can:
1) Learn from approaches they find helpful.
2) Understand and learn from their mistakes.
3) Discuss the best ways to manage overload.

Remember, we *all* feel overloaded from time to time – life cannot always be stable and predictable. Feel more and more confident that even when things get tough, you have the skills and positivity to keep going and to manage your overload.

Action plan for a new situation or stressful fear

We all come across *new situations,* which can make us nervous and stress us out. This could be a speech to give at a public occasion, a new journey to make or a job interview. Quite often, fear can lead us to avoid good preparation.

Many people also have *specific fears or phobias* that they feel incapable of overcoming, such as being afraid of spiders, the dark, the dentist or flying. Sometimes, the fear is so great that we avoid being in this situation or avoid being near the things we are afraid of.

When faced with any of the above situations, fear can go away on its own. When it doesn't, we often think and behave in a way which *keeps the fear going.* For example, the more we avoid going to the dentist because we are scared, the more difficult it becomes to eventually go.

There are two main methods we can use to overcome a fear: gradually facing (desensitisation) or confronting it head on and waiting for the level of anxiety to subside.

Desensitise the fear
Have you heard of the phrase: 'if you fail to prepare you are preparing to fail'? Well, that may sound dramatic, but it has some relevance when overcoming something we're afraid of. Desensitisation involves gradually facing up to a fear little by little through preparation and practice.

Let's use a common example of a fear that many of us share: *making a speech* at a work presentation or family celebration. You may immediately say you recognise this. If you don't, then try to understand the general principles, because it relates to many other fears you might have.

Preparation and *practice* will enable you to feel in control and be less anxious.

Making a speech: prepare so that you can reduce the anxiety or the 'stage fright':
1) Give yourself some time to sit quietly and think about what you need to do.
2) Be confident you can give a speech on the day if you prepare properly.
3) Break down the fear of giving a speech into *smaller bits* which will help you be more confident about tackling it. Put them into a 'ladder' with the easiest step at the bottom.
4) Work your way 'up the steps'.

It could look like this:

▲	Give the speech	▲
▲	Visualise giving the speech in the room (in your mind)	▲
▲	Practise the speech in the room in which you will give it (if possible)	▲
▲	Practise the speech in front of a friend	▲
▲	Practise the speech in front of a mirror	▲
▲	Practise reading the speech	▲
▲	Write drafts and complete speech	▲
▲	Preparation: What is the speech about?	▲
▲	Give yourself time	▲

The desensitisation approach can be used for any type of fear or new experience. The skill is to divide the fear or new experience into small steps to overcome it. For example, in the table below we have divided up the fears we mentioned earlier into some smaller steps.

FEAR	STEPS TO OVERCOME
Plane Travel	Visit an airport; watch planes take off; understand plane noises; imagine the take off; talk to friends about what it was like for them.
Dentist visit	Sit in a waiting room; understand dental equipment and sounds; talk to a friend about their recent visit; sit in a dentist's chair; arrange a simple check up.
Spider Fear	Look at spider pictures; look at a spider with a friend nearby; visit a zoo; watch a friend move a spider with a glass and card.
Post-accident travel fear	Sit in a parked car; relax on a short journey; tell yourself, 'I am safe' thoughts; go for a drive around an empty car park.
Job interview	Prepare likely questions and good answers; practise q/a with a friend; practise describing your strengths and weaknesses; practise walking in and sitting down.
Unfamiliar journey	Look at a map; discuss options with others; decide on best route; write yourself clear directions.

Just as we have said many times before, it is useful to consider what action you take in the four areas of your TLCB.

For example, taking the dentist visit, *remember:*
- **Your thinking** – Think positively and calmly about your ability to deal with visiting the dentist and managing your anxiety levels. Also consider how worthwhile a visit to the dentist will be.
- **Your lifestyle** – Manage your general health, including your eating, drinking and exercise, before your visit to the dentist. It all helps.
- **Your communication** – Be pleasant and talkative to the receptionist, dental nurse and dentist when you see them.
- **Your behaviour** – Breathe deeply and relax physically when you are in the waiting room and eventually when you are in the dentist chair.

Confront it.

In some situations it is difficult to prepare yourself and the most practical solution is to make yourself directly confront what you are afraid of. Although initially you are likely to feel very uncomfortable, this anxiety can't go on forever. It will subside eventually, especially with the realisation that nothing bad is going to happen to you.

By realising the long-term benefits and low risks, you may be encouraged to make this decision.

New situations crop up in our life on a fairly frequent basis. Some of these will make us nervous. In addition, all of us have things which frighten us and some of these will need dealing with. Have confidence that the techniques we have discussed here will help to keep them in your mental 'back pocket' to use when necessary.

Action plan for an everyday negative event

Despite efforts to manage stress on an everyday basis, at times you, like everyone else, will experience a particular event which upsets you. This could make your stress control 'wobble' and even make you feel 'this is the last straw'.

Examples of common unhappy events that might happen are:
- Argument with a member of your family.
- Argument with a friend or acquaintance.
- Monthly financial debt.
- Difficult child-care issue.
- Mechanical breakdown (in house, car or office).
- Medical problem (self or family member).
- Weight gain.
- Return from holiday.
- A hold up on a journey.
- Stress or significant change at work.
- Loss of something important.

As a result of an unhappy event occurring, you could again experience many of the symptoms of stress discussed at the beginning of this book (in Section 1).

This may make you think in a nervous, pessimistic way.

Your lifestyle may be affected – you may find yourself doing more stress-inducing activities (such as excessive alcohol consumption, smoking and eating unhealthy foodstuffs), while doing less stress-reducing activities (such as physical exercise, relaxation exercise, creative work and eating healthily).

You may forget to put into practice your communication skills and close yourself off from people. The interactions you do have with people may be short, negative and end up making you feel worse.

Your behaviour may be affected – you may *feel* physically anxious. You could also find that your ability to *do* things normally, effectively and efficiently is adversely affected.

All these effects are unpleasant but normal. It is also normal to try to do something to make yourself feel better.

What you can do:

Understand your stress.
The first step in any type of 'stress management' is to recognise and understand the "stressor". Most stressors are common to all of us. For example, at times we will all experience one or more of the stresses on the earlier list. Understanding this doesn't make the stress less but helps us to not feel 'abnormal'.

Use your thinking skills.
Put the event in context – try and think as logically as you can. However stressful it is, it is likely that the stress will pass or settle down either on its own or by your (and other people's) sensible handling. Frequently think to yourself in a positive and optimistic way that things will get

better. Use your problem solving skills to work out the best workable solution.

Use your lifestyle skills.
Make sure you 'keep your batteries charged' by eating and drinking healthily. If possible, have some exercise even if this is a quick walk around the block – the fresh air and activity will help you feel calmer, happier and more clear-headed.

Use your communication skills.
Reach out to one or two of your friends telling them what has happened, to get their reassurance and support. You could also discuss with them the possible solutions that you have come up with through your problem-solving, considering the 'pros' and 'cons'.

Use your behavioural skills.
Stay calm. Practise any type of relaxation, even 'taking a deep breath', on a regular basis.

Below we have applied this strategy to an unhappy event such as dealing with a large bill:

PROBLEM	WHAT TO DO
Unexpected lack of available funds this month to pay a big bill. You are worried about how to cope.	Stay calm. Review the financial situation and use your 6-step problem solving plan. Possible solutions: √ accuracy of bill. √ work more hours. √ options for payment – could you sell something or borrow the money? √ practical reductions in weekly spend. √ ways of reducing next month's costs. √ saying 'no' to costly invitations. √ monitor 'ins' and 'outs'. √ keep afloat generally with healthy lifestyle.

The stress associated with most unhappy events settles down and resolves itself over a period of time. We can learn from these types of events and increase our self-confidence. Paradoxically, after we have experienced many of these events, our personal resources increase and we become better at handling them.

We look at the following three events to consider some of the coping strategies you could use within the context of your 6-step problem-solving plan.

PROBLEM	WHAT TO DO
Argument with family member	Think clearly or write down what your side of the argument is. What is their side? Can you understand part of their opinion? What would make the situation a little better? Could you phone, text, email or write to them?
Car breakdown	Where is the nearest help (garage, breakdown service)? Can you phone someone (to let them know; to ask for help; get some support)? Consider whether to leave the car or organise immediate help. Tell yourself it will get sorted out and try deep breathing to stay calm. Minimise disruption by communicating what's happened to others.
Return from holiday	Anticipate that in 'X' hours you will be back on top of your jobs. Set realistic goals for getting necessary jobs done. Relax while you work. Reward yourself with periodic breaks such as a soft drink and healthy snack every 60 minutes.

Remember:
- ✓ **Your thinking skills:** Think calmly and positively that you will get through this crisis and that you can do several things to speed up this process. Use your 6-step problem-solving plan to work out what these are.
- ✓ **Your lifestyle skills:** Use eating, drinking and exercise to keep your batteries charged both mentally and physically.
- ✓ **Your communication skills:** Communicate with others – they will be sympathetic and understand what will help.
- ✓ **Your behavioural skills:** Relax while you are thinking what to do and then while doing it. Coping in a crisis is easier if you don't make it worse by adding more stressful feelings. Keep on top of your personal organisation too.

Action plan for a crisis event

When does an unhappy event become a 'catastrophe' or what we have called *a crisis event*? This is usually when the event involves major change and overwhelming feelings of loss, uncertainty or vulnerability. It can feel as if our whole sense of being and daily life routine is being challenged and we don't know how we are going to cope today or tomorrow. We typically feel very anxious and worried – experiencing feelings of panic and tearfulness.

The most difficult events we are likely to experience include:
- Death of a partner.
- Divorce or relationship separation.
- Death of a close family member (parent, child, sibling).
- Significant personal injury (accident at home, work, on the road, or ill-health).
- Redundancy or dismissal.
- Sexual problems.
- Business re-organisation or job change.
- Expected or planned events (retirement, marriage, pregnancy, child leaving home).
- Conflicts with 'significant people'.
- Relocation (house, school, location).

Whether expected or unexpected, a crisis event feels awful – we used the word *catastrophe* earlier because emotionally some events can feel like *the end of the world*. As described above, we can sometimes not know how we are going to cope over the next few hours or days. The level of stress is often great and will need the best stress management you can produce. Within hours and days of the event occurring, try to identify ways of dealing with some aspect of it.

If the event is expected - such as the death of a very ill relative, or scheduled redundancy or retirement – you may have had the opportunity to consider how you will feel and what you might do. These are preventative measures which can help you cope with the stress. The event, however, may still make you feel very distressed and 'lost' emotionally and unsure what to do.

If the event is unexpected and comes 'out of the blue', you yourself will not have been prepared for it or may not have any personal experience of it. However, you will be surprised how many people around you *will* have experienced this particular ocurrence and can give you good, helpful support if you talk to them. Talking can help you either by letting you air your feelings, or because the other person can be supportive or make helpful practical suggestions.

What you can do:

Use your thinking skills.
Accept that your emotional feelings and general unease are understandable in the circumstances – it is not silly or stupid or weak to have these feelings. It is logical that you will feel like this. It is also logical that you will start to feel gradually better soon.

Visualise that, whatever the outcome over the next few days, weeks or months, you will adjust and cope with what has happened in the best way you can. The stress will soon reduce to a more bearable level.

Stay as positive and optimistic as you can. Even though a crisis event is awful, the aftermath is as much affected by our own reaction to the event as to the event itself.

Can you apply your problem-solving skills to come up with some helpful ideas of how to sort out your situation, or just to cope better? Decide on your best next steps both *short-term* (get a good meal, go for a walk, phoning a friend) and *long-term* (reorganising your life, consideration of major life decisions).

Use your lifestyle skills.
Don't fall into the trap of drinking alcohol heavily and regularly. It may feel like it's helping when really it may just be compounding your

problems. Your rationality, productivity and general health may all suffer.

Try to maintain your healthy eating, sleeping and exercise routines as much as possible, even though you may not feel like it. These positive routines will help you remain calm.

Use your communication skills.
Reach out to your family and friends for reassurance and support. Tell them your fears – how you really feel – and discuss things through with them.

If you have come up with some short-term and long-term plans through your problem-solving technique, discuss those too.

Remember – even though this situation may be new and particularly frightening for you, others around you may have experienced a similar situation. Tap into this experience to help you cope with your situation.

Use your behavioural skills.
Stay calm. Practise any of the many stress reduction techniques you know, such as instant relaxation and PMR. Use them regularly whenever you can. Even if you are very distressed and agitated, relaxation will help.

Once you have tried a number of sensible coping strategies, you may find that your own personal resources, including the help and support from your friends and family, are insufficient to help you manage the stress associated with this event. If this happens, you may consider going to see your GP or an experienced therapist. However, you may be surprised what hitherto unrecognised inner resources you have when faced with a new and initially frightening life event.

Overleaf we have identified some short-term and longer-term coping strategies for dealing with three adverse life events: a relationship separation, redundancy and a big relationship conflict.

PROBLEM	WHAT TO DO
Relationship separation	Identify reasons for separation; project forward one week and one month – the feelings of loss will alter; discuss this event with a friend; reinforce your self esteem – tell yourself that you are a good person; do things that give you pleasure; try to socialise - maintain contact with friends and acquaintances; consider reconciliation options and/or final separation/move-on options; consider possible friendship with ex-partner; maintain contact with children (if any); maintain eating, hydration and exercise to encourage reasonable sleeping pattern.
Redundancy	Brainstorm possible options with partner or friend; consider how to access job guidance, advice or counselling; anticipate you will get further job options; see this event in positive 'it's an opportunity' light – many career successes follow this type of crisis; maintain eating, hydration and exercise.
Big relationship conflict	Identify reasons for conflict (your opinion, their opinion); discuss conflict with a friend; keep conflict in perspective; identify good aspects of your relationship; set up some communication channels; communicate if possible about neutral topics; take a 'one down' position over the major issue; don't blame or criticise the other person.

For most people, crisis events are rare. You can prepare yourself to a certain extent by reading this section and also by watching those around you and how they cope. Be confident that if and when a very stressful crisis event happens to you, you have the skills to manage the stress.

Affirmation card (1)

....

....

....

....

....

....

....

Affirmation card

(2)

....

....

....

....

....

....

....

....

Diary pages

....

....

....

....

....

....

....

....

....

....

....

....

....

....

....

....

···

···

···

···

···

···

···